Modern Tractors
Close Up

Modern Tractors
Close Up

Stephen Richmond
and
Jonathan Whitlam

Second Sight Productions

First published 2007
Copyright Stephen Richmond and Jonathan Whitlam 2007

ISBN 978-0-9557367-0-4
A catalogue record for this book is available from the British Library

Published by Second Sight Productions
Station House, 1 Station Road
Tiptree, Essex, CO5 OAD, United Kingdom

Design and Art Direction by Marc De'ath | The Creative Coop
Typeset by The Creative Coop
Printed and bound by Colourplan Print and Design Ltd, Ipswich

Author's Note
All the horsepower ratings given in this book are approximate and should be used as a guide only. Wherever possible we
have given maximum power ratings, which on the latest tractors is often considerably more than the rated horsepower and
is often only available at the p.t.o., which can lead to some confusion. We have tried to make sure that all the information in
this book is as correct as possible but it is not designed to be used as an operator's manual.

Disclaimer
This book has been published in good faith and whilst every effort has been taken to ensure the accuracy of the
information enclosed, the authors and publishers cannot accept responsibility for any errors, inaccuracies or omissions
contained herein, or for the consequences of any reliance on the information provided by the same. The views expressed
by the authors do not necessarily represent the views of Second Sight Productions

Preface

It is just over ten years since we released our first book. Modern Tractors was published back in 1996 and so it seemed that it was about time for a sequel.

Much to our amazement, Modern Tractors went on to become something of a bestseller. We had thought, wrongly as it turned out, that we were in the minority when it came to liking tractors of the 1960's, 70's, 80's, and 90's. Subsequently we went on to produce five more books and we've featured in many DVD programmes based around the tractor theme.

For several years people have been asking us when we will be releasing another book because, even though many years have passed, it seems that there is still a gap in the market for the modern tractor devotee. It has always been our intention to follow up our first book but our spare time has been taken up with DVD production, hence the long gestation period. We certainly didn't lack material. We continued taking photographs and the ten thousand pictures we had in 1996 have now more than tripled. It was just a question of finding the time to put it all together.

Anyway here it is, Modern Tractors – Close-up. Readers of our first offering will immediately notice some differences. Firstly, we have limited the period covered by this volume to tractors introduced since 1990 - if we increased it to more than this there would be just too many machines it fit

in. It was also a necessity because technology moves so fast these days that tractor models are replaced every couple of years or so instead of lasting ten! Secondly, the book is a different format. We wanted to show much more of the machines in question and try to give a feel for what they are like inside the cab as well as out and an upright design suits this style. Despite these changes we hope that the original concept of the first book still shines through – a celebration of what the modern tractor is and does.

So sit back and enjoy a look at farming's front liners of the last seventeen years. It's an absorbing story and we hope this book will continue to satisfy tractor enthusiasts both young and old for many years to come.

Acknowledgements
We would like to thank all the farmers, contractors, dealers and farm workers who have allowed us to take pictures of their machinery over the last ten years or so. We also would like to thank Cheffins Auctioneers in Cambridgeshire, for access to the amazing array of tractors at their monthly sales in Sutton and Bill Pepper in particular. And of course, we have to thank Alan James of Second Sight Productions who has made all this possible.

An Introduction

So what is a modern tractor? Well, for the purposes of this book we have taken it as a tractor introduced since the dawn of the 1990s, a fairly arbitrary line in the sand perhaps, but one that hopefully makes sense. The problem is, of course, time, what we consider as modern today will one day be classed as vintage, however hard that concept might be to grasp!

We have always thought it strange that the tractor movement seems to be only interested in what they class as 'vintage' tractors. At the large shows held every year the mid-70s is seen as the break off point, with tractors before then known as vintage and anything built after them, classed as modern.

Time has moved on and we like to class tractors in a slightly different fashion, probably because of our age! To us vintage tractors are those built from the very early days up to 1960. The next group we call classic tractors and these take us through the 1960s, 70s and 80s leaving the modern category to run from 1990 to the present day. Now, we know that not everyone is going to agree with this grouping, but to us it at least gives a starting point and does not alienate those who collect tractors built since the 1970s as the current thinking seems to do.

CLOCKWISE FROM TOP RIGHT:

1960s A true classic, the little Massey Ferguson 135.

1970s Complete with quiet Q cab, the Ford 3600.

1980s Midrange power house, Marshall 904XL.

1990s Green machine, the John Deere 6600.

21st Century - Mean machine, the Claas Ares 697ATZ.

Of course, the term 'modern tractor' is one that has moved with the times and must continue to do so as time passes.

Back in 1917, the new Fordson Model F was seen as the very latest in tractor design, with mass production and the principle of unitary construction both being new ideas. Harry Ferguson launched the Type A in 1936 – the first production tractor in the world to offer a three-point linkage and hydraulic control. This was the very latest in tractor technology. Other companies introduced the power take off shaft and diesel power, while crawler tractors and four wheel drive machines vied for top spot on many heavy land farms. The arrival of the first safety cabs in the 1970s meant that the modern tractor was now much safer for the driver and he stayed warmer in the winter! But perhaps the major step towards what we call a modern tractor today was the introduction of electronic controls. Massey Ferguson were one of the first to jump into the microchip age, with the introduction of the 2005 Electronic series in the early 1980s and they followed that up with the introduction of the 3000 Series in 1986.

These new machines not only offered electronic control of the hydraulics but also a computerised management system of all the tractors main functions. This was nothing short of a revolution and, by the beginning of the next decade, most manufacturers would be offering something similar on their own machines. The modern tractor – as we know it - had arrived!

ANTI-CLOCKWISE FROM TOP LEFT:

The Fordson Model F, the tractor that set new standards back in 1917.

The Ferguson Brown, the tractor that began a revolution in farming.

The MF 3000 Series helped to usher in a new age of electronics, with the midrange 3080 model being one of the most popular.

But the 1990s was a very different place from that of the previous decade, the tractor world was now changing at a very hectic pace as mergers and takeovers began to bite. The beginning of the new decade was marked by the surprise announcement that Ford New Holland had been sold to Fiat, making it one of the largest farm machinery companies in one fell swoop. This opened the floodgates to further rationalisation as Case IH (itself formed by the merger of J. I Case and International Harvester in 1985) bought the Austrian tractor maker Steyr, adding it to a portfolio that already included the North American producer of giant tractors – Steiger. Massey Ferguson was bought by AGCO, a company steeped in a rich tapestry of American tractor manufacturers including Allis-Chalmers, Minneapolis-Moline, Oliver and White. AGCO then went on to purchase Fendt in Germany, the rights to the Challenger rubber tracked crawler range from Caterpillar and even the Finnish tractor firm Valtra. In Italy, Same had already acquired firms like Lamborghini and Hurlimann in previous decades, but now they moved up a gear with the purchase of the German Deutz Fahr agricultural operations. Renault worked closely with John Deere for a time before being bought out by Claas, while John Deere itself remained aloof from mergers and takeovers and stayed fiercely independent, something that helped it gain a large percentage of market share the world over, while all the other firms caused problems for themselves by rationalising and downsizing their combined product ranges. Then, in 1999 the world shook with the mega merger of Case IH and New Holland as Fiat went after the big guns with the purchase of the American Case IH group to form CNH.

ANTI-CLOCKWISE FROM TOP LEFT:
David Brown 1490: David Brown taken over and merged with J.I. Case in 1972.
IH 484: International Harvester merged with Case in 1985.
Case IH Maxxum 5130: New Case IH tractors appeared from 1988.
Fiat 1380: Number one in Europe foe many years.
Ford 8830: Ford New Holland a global full liner.
Opposite right:
New Holland 7840:Fiat and Ford joined forces as New Holland in 1991.

All this excitement has made the last sixteen years or so very busy indeed. And it hasn't been all good. We have seen the names of many well known manufacturers disappear for ever, we have also seen the disappearance of factories like that at Banner Lane in Coventry, the once proud home of the famous little grey fergie and many later favourites like the 200, 300 and 4200 Series tractors. But it's not all doom and gloom, as the market remains competitive and the farmer can still get a good new or used tractor deal. There has even been room for a new tractor manufacturer, McCormick having set up production in the Case IH plant at Doncaster that had to be sold on following the CNH merger. Owned by ARGO the Italian owners of Landini, McCormick started with the old Case IH Maxxum and CX tractor lines and is now producing new designs of up to 280hp, all built in Doncaster until production was shifted to Italy in 2007.

Over in Staffordshire, JCB have made a huge success of their Fastrac – a tractor designed as much for the road as the field, and one that is popular not only in this country but also many other places, especially Germany.

ANTI CLOCKWISE FROM TOP RIGHT:

New Holland 8360: Six cylinder models built in Basildon

Case IH Maxxum MX110: MX Series built in Doncaster

New Holland TM155: Case New Holland formed in 1999

Case IH MXM155: Now built in Basildon

Tractor innovations have become much more sophisticated over the last ten years, with features such as front axle suspension, cab suspension, computer management systems, satellite navigation and constantly variable transmissions and even the tracklayer has made a comeback with the advent of the rubber track concept.

Some tractor enthusiasts think that the tractors of today are all the same - look the same, sound the same and are built the same, but we disagree! Things are only just beginning to hot up and, even if there are fewer manufacturers than twenty years ago, there are many more options, models and horse power ranges available today than previously, as the humble farm tractor moves on into the 21st century - more powerful, more efficient and more fascinating than ever before!

FROM TOP:

Fendt Vario 818: Stepless transmission, electronically controlled luxury.
JCB Fastrac 3185: All round suspension, fast speed, large comfortable cab equals the ultimate in versatility.
Challenger MT765: Rubber tracks, equals great traction with fast road speeds

Case International Maxxum

The Maxxum range was launched in 1990. It was only the second completely new type of tractor to be introduced by the company formed in 1985 by the merger of International Harvester and J.I. Case. The Maxxum 5100 Series was a three model strong mid-range line-up of tractors and included the 90hp four cylinder 5120, the 100hp 5130 and the 110hp 5140, all powered by Cummins six cylinder diesels. The Maxxums were the first mid-size tractors to feature a clutchless shuttle on a semi-powershift 16 x 12 speed transmission and, although they were made in the German factory they were in many ways the spiritual successor to the old Case IH 94 Series that had been built in the David Brown plant in Meltham, Yorkshire up to 1988.

Fiatagri Winner

Fiat's long running 90 Series was showing its age by 1990 and the all-new Winner range replaced the 100 to 130hp models in that year. This is the baby of the range, the 100hp F100 powered by a six cylinder Iveco engine. Several transmission options were available on the new tractors including a 16 x 16 or a 32 x 32 creeper option. This was topped off by a completely new cab, which gave much better all round visibility than the outgoing machines. All the Winner tractors were made in Italy.

Renault 54 Series

From the French corner comes the Renault 54 Series that replaced the long lasting 14 Series models in 1990. This middle of the range 110-54 TZ has 100hp available from its six cylinder MWM power plant, and is also equipped with the amazing Hydrostable cab that first appeared in 1989 on the 14 Series. This clever system uses four springs on each corner to cushion the whole cab from shocks produced by riding over rough ground. It provides the driver with an extremely comfortable ride and one that was unbeatable at the time of its introduction. Our example here is busy collecting peas from a large Ploeger EPD 520 pea harvester ready to ferry them away to waiting road transport.

Taking a closer look at the 54 Series we see that the front nose cone raises for easy access to the engine air filter making servicing much easier. Inside the Hydrostable cab, the gear and shuttle levers are clearly visible as are the spool valve levers and the numerous buttons on the dashboard that control the windscreen wipers, hazard lights and on-board computer system. This particular tractor is the 135hp 145-54 model, once again powered by a six cylinder MWM diesel.

For those farmers wishing for something that stands out from the crowd, Renault offered the Nectra with its distinctive silver paint job and full specification. Taking a rest from ploughing and pressing, this 145hp 155-54 Nectra dates from 1992.

Lamborghini Formula

It may not have the same speed as the cars that it takes its name from, but it definitely has Italian flair and good looks. The 115hp six cylinder Formula 115 has no difficulty in pulling a four furrow Ransomes plough or an articulated bale trailer across the stubble during harvest time. This range of tractors replaced the older 6 Series machines and introduced new styling, engines and cabs as well as more electronic functions. Gearbox options included a 36 x 36 or 48 x 48 speed transmission controlled by three separate gear levers- one for the forward and reverse shuttle, another for main range selection incorporating a three speed powershift button and one further lever for the high, medium and low range selection.

The biggest in the new Formula line-up was the turbocharged 135. To get its 135hp down to the ground while preparing a seedbed for sugar beet with a Lely Roterra power harrow, this farmer has equipped the 135 with eight wheels, a trick that also helps to spread the tractors weight over a larger area and avoid soil compaction. On closer inspection of the bonnet, a tall air intake and cleaner bowl becomes evident, something that is missing from the smaller 115. Also several badges can be seen including a 40kph badge and the word 'zinc', indicating the zinc coating that has been given to the tinwork to reduce corrosion. For many years Lamborghini has been owned by Same, another Italian firm that also owns the Swiss Hurlimann tractor brand.

Track Marshall TM 200

This imposing beast is the British answer to the rubber tracked Caterpillar Challenger crawler introduced in the late 1980s. Powered by a six cylinder Cummins 8.3 litre 210hp diesel engine driving through a 16 x 2 powershift transmission, the TM 200 should have been a thorn in the Cat's side when launched in 1990. Unfortunately insufficient development and the unsure future of the Track Marshall company led to few being built. The design actually hails from Australia were it was built by the Waltanna organisation, Track Marshall building it in the UK under license. Only a few larger 250hp versions were built, production ceasing in 1994 despite the well thought-out design of these tractors which included a tiltable cab that made access to major components for servicing and repair much simpler.

JCB HMV

Several studies carried out during the 1980s highlighted the fact that modern tractors spent nearly, if not more of their time on the road, than on the field. Several tractor makers had tried to cater for this, most noticeably Mercedes Benz with their Unimog and MB Trac machines, while Trantor was making transport tractors back in the late 70s. Towards the end of the 1980s British heavy plant manufacturer JCB was busy designing their own solution to the transport tractor riddle. Their idea was not only to produce a tractor with a high road speed capability, but also to back this up with a fully suspended chassis and air braking system, producing a machine that was just as at home in a field with a plough as out on the road. Several prototypes were built, including this one seen at JCB's own test site in Staffordshire. Originally known as the High Mobility Vehicle, this was the machine that would eventually become the Fastrac.

JCB Fastrac

The 1990 Smithfield Show saw the unveiling of the JCB Fastrac. The largest of the two new models was the 147hp 145 Turbo seen here which, like the 117hp 125 model, was fitted with a six cylinder Perkins motor. The new tractors were brimming with new features, not least of which was the 40 mph top speed! Others included full all-round suspension, front linkage, spacious two-man cab and a large load platform behind it. Inside the cab, two main gearlevers operated the 36 x 24 speeds and the hydraulics were electronically controlled by a Bosch Hitch-Tronic system. At its launch the Fastrac caused quite a stir and soon became an unqualified success particularly in the UK and Germany.

John Deere 55 Series

Well-established firm John Deere introduced the 55 Series high horsepower tractors in 1990. Built in America, these giants had power aplenty as well as full powershift transmissions. The 4255 was fitted with a 155hp six cylinder Deere power pack, giving it more than enough grunt to haul a large slurry tanker complete with huge injecting tines. Largest of the 55 Series were the 190hp 4755 and 228hp 4955. These machine's huge bonnets were made more imposing by John Deere placing the exhausts up beside the cab, leaving an unobstructed view across the large hood. This did however, negate the SG2 cabs feature of a central pillar running down the front!

Landini 80 Series

Italian firm Landini's association with Massey Ferguson is evident throughout the 80 Series models, not only with the 600 Series cab from the early 1980s, but also with the Perkins four cylinder motor under the blue hood. The 8880's power plant pumps out 80hp and drives through the Powerflow 12 x 4 syncromesh transmission. The cab is fitted with many standard features such as deluxe fully adjustable seat, heater, tiltable steering column and front/rear work lights. Optional equipment includes creeper transmissions, giving a maximum of 36 x 12 gears as well as the Landtronic electronic linkage controls and digital dashboard.

Ford 40 Series

Ford needed a radical new design to replace the best selling 10 Series, and they succeeded in 1991 with the introduction of the 40 Series, even though by now the company was largely owned by Fiat, after the Ford New Holland and Fiatagri merger. Claiming to be new from the ground up, the 40 Series spanned six models from 75 to 120hp, with both six cylinder and four cylinder power plants that were also completely new and dubbed PowerStar. Built in Basildon in Essex the 40 Series tractors were also available in two forms - SL and SLE. This 85hp four cylinder 6640 SL formed part of the more basic SL range and includes a SyncroShift Dual Power transmission giving 24 x 24 gears. It is seen hard at work with a Kuhn power harrow preparing a seedbed for wheat.

The two largest tractors in the range were the 8240 and 8340, both only being offered in SLE form. This meant that they were fitted with the new electronic ElectroShift transmission giving 16 x 16 speeds, as well as the ElectroLink electronic hydraulic controls. The 8240 featured a 110hp six cylinder PowerStar engine, while inside the new SuperLux cab, all the main controls for the SLE version are positioned to the driver's right, including the four orange levers which control the high and low ranges, four speed powershift complete with operating buttons, forward and reverse shuttle and hand throttle. The lever nearest the seat controls the rear linkage arms up and down movement, while the four levers above this are the controls for the four spool valves. The yellow knob is the power-take-off on/off control, which is positioned next to the two rocker switches that activate four wheel drive and diff lock. Next comes the main console that houses the ElectroLink hydraulic controls.

Caterpillar Challenger C Series

The American construction machinery giant Caterpillar, revolutionised the world of the agricultural crawler with the launch of the Challenger 65 rubber tracked machine at the end of the 1980s. In 1993 Caterpillar re-launched it as the 65C and also introduced a larger tractor, the Challenger 75C complete with CAT turbocharged and intercooled six cylinder 325hp motor. This example is using a Kverneland eleven furrow plough and belongs to a Suffolk farmer and contractor. The rubber tracks allowed the crawler to travel at speed on the road, something that was completely unheard of with the old steel tracked machines. A year later the 355hp Challenger 85C made its appearance.

Massey Ferguson 3600 Series

American owned Massey Ferguson also offered large tractors, albeit with wheels instead of tracks. Two heavy weights made their appearance in the early 1990s the smallest of which was the 170hp 3670 seen here about to turn on the headland with a Dowdeswell five-furrow plough and Claydon furrow cracker..

The flagship of the range was the 190hp 3690. Like the 3670 these tractors differed from the rest of the Massey Ferguson range in that Valmet six cylinder engines were fitted instead of the usual Perkins units. Standard features on these tractors included the Datatronic electronic monitoring system with its controls mounted on the left hand side cab pillar, the 32 x 32 Dynashift transmission system that gave four main ranges in high and low with four powershift gears in each of the four ranges both in forward and reverse. These were imposing machines, the length of the bonnet being exaggerated by the distinctive sloping nose at the front.

23

Lamborghini Racing

Above: Italian firm Same also launched new models in 1992 with the introduction of the virtually identical Same Titan, Lamborghini Racing and Hurlimann Master ranges. The Lamborghini version of this common platform design is shown at work with a Gregoire Besson seven furrow plough, traction being helped by water ballasted tyres. These new tractors were very advanced and featured a host of electronic controls, including an electronic engine governor for its six cylinder 165hp turbocharged and intercooled Lamborghini power unit. One joystick controlled the hydraulics and the 27 x 27 powershift transmission.

John Deere 6000 & 7000 Series

Below: In 1992 John Deere replaced nearly all its tractor models in one fell swoop with the launch of the 6000 and 7000 Series machines. The smaller 6000 tractors were made in Germany and the largest 6400 model is seen here at work with a KeyAg potato planter. Fitted with a four cylinder 100hp Deere power plant, this was a compact and reasonably light tractor for its size. New from the ground up, the 6000 Series featured a brand new TechCentre cab, exhaust mounted to the side of it and the PowrQuad gearbox that offered several different transmission options. The 7800 was the largest tractor in the new 7000 range of high horsepower tractors with its six cylinder 170hp Deere motor. Built in North America these machines followed the design cues of the smaller 6000 models, but everything was much bigger. A full powershift PowrQuad transmission was a standard feature and was controlled by a single lever. John Deere tractors had a strong following in Britain, but with the launch of these two new ranges even more farmers and contractors would be turning to the green and yellow machines than ever before..

Case IH 95 Series

Despite the launch of the all new Magnum and Maxxum ranges, new versions of the older International Harvester models were re-incarnated as the 95 Series, replacing the older 85 Series machines. Built in Doncaster these new models benefited from a restyled front grill, cab roof, revised colour scheme and digital dashboard but otherwise were basically unchanged from the outgoing models. This two wheel drive example of the 82hp four cylinder 895 is dubbed Super and is seen for sale at the Cheffins agricultural machinery sale in Cambridgeshire.

This four wheel drive 895 carries the name Duo on its cab door, denoting a special promotion on these models in the early 1990s. The XL cab fitted to these tractors dates back many years and apart from the few cosmetic changes, remained the same until the demise of the bigger 1455 XL tractor later in the decade. The 895 was fitted with a two speed Torque Amplifier powershift transmission, giving the tractor a total of 16 x 8 gears. A creeper box was optional, but not specified on this particular tractor, something that would have been useful while working with this Reekie 200 de-stoner!

Massey Ferguson
3000 & 3100 Series

This smaller 3075 is also engaged in potato work, this time preparing the soil with a bedformer before the crop is planted. Launched in 1993 this tractor replaced the 3070 with a 98hp four cylinder turbocharged Perkins engine and the Dynashift transmission. The 3075 would prove to be the last new model to be introduced before the arrival of completely new models two years later. Unfortunately this tractor is no more as it caught fire while corn carting and was completely burnt out three years after this picture was taken.

This view inside the cab shows the gear lever layout of the new 3000 Series tractors, basically much the same as the bigger 3670 and 3690 we saw earlier. The 3120 model was also introduced in 1993 and featured a six cylinder 120hp Perkins Quadram engine. The 3120, designed as a light weight but powerful machine, had effectively replaced the 115hp 3115 but was considerably less weighty than the contemporary 126hp 3125 model. The 120hp power bracket was destined to become the most popular choice for customers as average horsepower continued to increase during the 1990s.

John Deere 6000 Series

Above and Right: 1993 saw further models join the John Deere 6000 Series. Also made in Germany, the new machines were six cylinder tractors and usurped the 6400 as the biggest tractor in the range. This 110hp 6600 is fitted with eight wheels and a front linkage to which is mounted a Lynx Sumo press. Another John Deere basks in the summer sun with a trailer while waiting for the combine, but this time it is the new flagship 6000 model - the 120hp 6800. Both new tractors carried on the styling and features of the four cylinder machines.

Same Titan

Right: The Titan 190 became the flagship model with 189hp from its turbocharged and intercooled Same block. As with the Lamborghini Racing models these tractors featured a high level of electronic sophistication as well as typical Italian styling flair.

Renault 54 Series

Above: With a straight six MWM 100hp engine, the 106-54 TL was a compact but powerful machine and found this Dowdeswell five furrow plough well within its capabilities. Built in France, the 106-54 was offered with a 16 x 16 mechanical splitter gearbox and a Syncrhronised shuttle reverser.

Lamborghini Racing

Left: The white alternative to the Titan was of course the Racing 190. Same's common platform design policy would be a sign of things to come by the 21st Century when some of the larger tractor manufacturers would follow Same down this route that cut manufacturing costs and made spare part supplies much more economical. Although never universally popular in the UK these machines were definitely impressive tractors, an image enhanced by this 190 complete with front and back drilling outfit. As with the Massey Ferguson 3075 we saw earlier, this tractor was unlucky enough to be the victim of a catastrophic fire only a few years into its life and is sadly no more. A single lever controls all the Racing's main functions electronically giving fingertip control.

Fendt Favorit 800 Series

Below: Built in Germany, Fendt tractors have a reputation as expensive premium tractors – the Rolls-Royce of the tractor world, with a high level of sophistication fitted as standard. The Favorit 800 Series was launched in 1993 and included the 190hp 818 featured here. Although still very business-like in design, these new models replaced the older, more box like 600 Series and now came with updated modern cabs that featured an all round suspension system and pillar mounted exhaust and air intake. All the tractors functions were electronically controlled including the 44 x 44 transmission, with power coming from a six cylinder MAN diesel.

Fiatagri 94 Series

Right: Fiatagri, now firmly linked with Ford New Holland, introduced the 94 Series in 1993 as smaller companions to the six cylinder Winner range. These were fairly simple four cylinder tractors built at Modena in Italy and replaced the smaller 90 Series models, although they were basically just updated versions of the outgoing machines. New Winner like bonnet styling gave a much more modern appearance however and they soon became relatively popular, especially with livestock farmers. This 85hp 88-94 is busy with a Claas Markant square baler.

Valmet Mezzo

Below: Valmet tractors from Finland have a long pedigree dating back to Bolinder Munktell, through the Volvo BM years and then the Valmet line up. With their own six cylinder turbo charged engines built in-house, 36 x 36 gearbox and a choice of colour schemes as well as a huge list of optional extras, these machines are something special. With personalised sign writing on the side of the cab roof, this 103hp 8400 negotiates the headland of a field with a Deutz Fahr combine in hot pursuit.

JCB Fastrac

Right: New flagship of the Fastrac range in 1993, was the Perkins powered 150hp, six cylinder turbocharged 155-65 that featured a 36 x 12 gearbox, made up by using high, medium and low range ratios. The whole Fastrac range was updated in this year and featured the new look as modelled here, waiting to collect its load of barley from the combine. Still embodying the principles of the original Fastrac concept, these tractors took the technology up a level and helped to further cement the idea of a fast transport tractor that was still capable of everyday farm work.

Ford 70 Series

Back in 1989, Ford launched the 30 Series high horsepower tractors that were based on the old TW Series machines, but featured a brand new and revolutionary gearbox. At the beginning of 1994 their replacements appeared, the brand new 70 Series. Built in the Versatile plant in Canada, these tractors were new from the ground up, still incorporating the Funk 18 x 9 gearbox that first appeared in 1989, but now with automatic operation in tenth gear by pushing the Auto button on the control panel. Spanning models from 170 to 240hp, another new feature included the option of SuperSteer - a new type of front axle that allowed a 65 degree turning circle, much better than the standard 55 degrees. Baby of the range was the 8670 while the 8770 turned in a respectable 190 horses and they all simply bristled with electronics controlled by no less than three on-board micro- computers.

John Deere 3000 Series

Right: It might be green and yellow but under the paint work of this John Deere 3100 resides a French built member of the Renault Ceres range. This was a result of a marketing agreement between the two companies concerning this four-model range of tractors. This 55hp three cylinder 3100, is fitted out for grassland duties and like the rest of the range is powered by a Deere Power Systems direct injection diesel engine.

Deutz Fahr Agroxtra/Agrostar

Right, below right and opposite bottom: German firm Deutz Fahr started a new trend in 1990, when they launched the AgroXtra range of six tractors from 60 to 113hp. What was so special about these tractors? Well, they had very prominently sloping bonnets, so sloping in fact that at some angles it was hard to tell where the engine was located. Gearbox options included an 18 x 6 or a 24 x 6 creeper version. By 1993 more sloping bonneted tractors arrived, and these were now fitted with the premium AgroStar cab that included tinted glass, aero fit seat and the AgroTronic i1 information centre. This 107hp six cylinder 6.08 model, is shown harvesting sugar beet with a Matrot six row topper and sugar beet harvester.

With the topper unit mounted on the tractors front linkage, it is easy to see the main benefit of the sloping bonnet design – much better visibility of front mounted implements and easy use of front loaders. Less space under the bonnet did lead to problems such as battery positioning and more importantly the need for an uprated cooling system, but the idea was so successful that several other manufacturers followed Deutz's lead and produced sloping bonnet models of their own, but never with the same amount of dedication as the instigators. By 1995 Deutz Fahr had been bought by Italian firm Same and became amalgamated to form Same Deutz Fahr.

Landini Legend

Left and below: Another Italian tractor maker, Landini had strong links with Massey Ferguson for many years, so much so that they produced out of date versions of Massey Ferguson models as their own and also made prodigious use of Perkins diesel engines. Eventually they needed to design their own machines and this they achieved with remarkable style when the Legend series appeared in 1994. The 115hp Legend 115, was one of the first introduced and featured a six cylinder Perkins motor and 36 x 36 transmission.

Fiat Winner

New Winner models appeared in 1993, including a new flagship model - the 140hp six cylinder F140 powered by an Iveco diesel. Its standard 12 x 12 transmission could be boosted with a creeper box to give a total of 24 x 12 gears. All the major controls are positioned to the driver's right including the gear levers, shuttle, hydraulic controls, etc. The original brown Fiatagri badge positioned on the radiator grill, changed colour to blue from 1995 to reflect the growing amalgamation of the Fiat and Ford tractor lines.

Caterpillar Challenger

The launch of Caterpillar's smaller rubber tracked crawlers in 1994 caused quite a stir. Seen with a six metre wide Dowdeswell power harrow, the Challenger 35 was powered by a CAT six cylinder 205hp motor, while the bigger 45, ploughing with a Gregoire Besson eight furrow, was endowed with 235hp. Apart from the rubber tracks and the CAT engines, these tractors used many of the parts found in the Ford New Holland 70 Series and Fiatagri G Series wheeled tractors also introduced in 1994. In fact, the crawlers were built on the same production line at the Versatile factory in Winnipeg, Canada. Ford acquired Versatile, renowned for their huge articulated tractors, back in 1987.

Lamborghini Premium

Above: New mid-range tractors from Lamborghini were dubbed Premium and spanned 85 to 105hp. Only the biggest – the 1060 shown here carting wheat away from the combine, was fitted with a six cylinder motor, the others featuring four cylinder units. The bonnet now had a pronounced slope and the cab was the same as fitted to the larger Formula models. Several transmission options were topped by an amazing 60 x 60 version, giving the operator plenty of choice whatever task was being carried out.

Lamborghini Racing

Left: Another model had appeared in the Racing series by this time. The entry level Racing 150 featured 150hp from its six cylinder motor and shared the same level of electronic sophistication as its bigger brothers.

JCB Fastrac

Above: Also in 1994 Staffordshire based JCB launched the biggest Fastrac yet. Its 170hp came from a six cylinder turbocharged and intercooled Cummins engine, instead of the Perkins units used on all Fastracs up until now. It carried on the Fastrac tradition of the earlier models but now had the extra power to cope with much larger machinery. This model included a 36 x 12 transmission and was available in either 40 or 45 mph versions.

Same Silver

Middle: In line with the common platform design policy, Same's version of the Premium range were known as Silver, despite being painted the usual deep red! Second in size in the new range was the four cylinder 90hp Same Silver shown here on demonstration with a Westmac mower. Hurlimann tractors were also based on these machines and were known as the XT range.

Same Titan

Right: Equivalent to the Racing range from Lamborghini comes the Titan 145, which was a red version of the 150 model. Specification was virtually identical between the two marques. Which do you prefer - red or white?

John Deere 8000 Series

Above: 1994 was also the year in which John Deere launched the all-new 8000 Series tractors. These large machines were most noticeable for their patented full frame design, where the engine and transmission was supported on a steel chassis, giving much more strength. There were four models, with the largest pumping out 260hp. The entry level model was the 185hp 8100. Next came the 8200 with 210hp on tap, while this 230hp 8300 looks very impressive with all round dual wheels fitted while subsoiling. All featured six cylinder Deere power plants that were turbocharged and intercooled, and were mounted well forward over the front axle to maximise weight distribution. Bristling with electronic controls in the new CommandArm console, the 8000 Series featured a powershift transmission giving 16 x 5 gears and a top speed of 24mph.

John Deere 6000 Series

Right: A new model was also added to the smaller 6000 Series, but this was by no means any lightweight! The 6900 featured 130hp from its six pot motor and was equipped with a beefed up front axle and extra pto clutches, to befit a tractor that replaced the physically larger 7600 machine. This 6900 is shown here powering a JF forage harvester, a job where plenty of power is needed at the pto, while in the cab the controls were laid out on a console to the driver's right and would make any previous 6000 Series driver feel immediately at home.

Case International Maxxum Plus 5100 Series

Above and left: 1995 saw the Case Maxxum range revamped with the new Plus models. This 100hp six cylinder Maxxum 5130 Plus, is seen at work with a Gregoire Besson five furrow plough. Inside the cab all the main controls are mounted on a pedestal to the right of the driving seat. The German built Maxxum range had proved very popular since their introduction five years previously and the Plus range saw them mature into very reliable and work thirsty machines. Flagship Maxxum was still the 125hp 5150, but it also received the Plus treatment including a neutral position on the forward and reverse shuttle and the new style decals. Note the substantial front linkage fitted to this 5150.

Mercedes Benz Unimog

Left: Although looking very much like a truck, this machine is also a very capable tractor, fitted with front and rear linkages and pto's, four wheel drive, load platform behind the cab and powerful six cylinder engines reaching up into the 200hp bracket. However in this country, despite its versatility, the Unimog is more often used in the industrial sector rather than mainstream agriculture.

Ford New Holland 40 Series

Left: By now the 100hp six cylinder Ford 7840 was becoming just as popular as the 7810 model that it replaced. This SLE version shows off some of the changes that were gradually made to the 40 Series as Fiat started to integrate the Fiat and Ford ranges. These included a blue roof instead of the previous white painted version and the use of the blue Fiatagri leaf on the front instead of the Ford roundal.

Renault 94 Series

Below and left: The 150hp 160-94 TZ followed the new flagship 170hp 180-94 model into production and shared it's styling and high-tech transmission. Power comes from a six cylinder MWM motor while Same built the MULTISHIFT 27 x 27 transmission in Italy. The control levers for the gearbox look very unconventional, and are housed in a moveable console to the right of the driver that also contains the push button controls for operating the four wheel drive engagement, pto control, diff-lock and computerised self-diagnostic system. Later tractors were also available in Renault's Tracfor series, these tractors being easily told apart from standard models by the white middle cab pillar and the Tracfor decal on the bonnet sides.

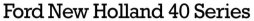

Fendt Xylon

Below: Based in Germany, the Fendt company had always been at the forefront of tractor design technology and had never shied away from specialist type machines, such as its long running range of toolcarrier tractors. But in 1994 the first production models of an even more radical design of tractor appeared – the Xylon. With a centrally fitted cab placed over a mid-mounted 4.6 litre turbocharged and intercooled four cylinder MAN diesel engine, plenty of room was left behind the cab for a load platform - ideal for de-mountable sprayers and fertiliser distributors or even seed hoppers, while at the front, a completely unobstructed forward view was available while using front mounted implements on the factory fitted integral front linkage. Also a factory fitted option, was the front axle suspension system, which gave greater comfort when travelling at the top road speed of 50kph. Despite three models from 110 to 140hp, the new concept failed to really catch on and the Xylon was phased out in the early years of the new century.

JCB Fastrac 1000 Series

Left: By 1995 the Fastrac had become an unqualified success, but despite this, the otherwise brilliant design did have some drawbacks. One of the greatest complaints from drivers was the large turning circle needed, especially during fieldwork as it meant a larger headland was required. Another factor was the comparatively high price of the Fastrac, when compared to equal size horsepower conventional machines. JCB's answer was a new type of smaller Fastrac – cue the 1115.

This was a lighter, more compact vehicle but also one that was still powerful and fast on the road, though not quite as athletic as its bigger predecessors. With a smaller cab and less sophisticated, but still fully suspended chassis, the overall cost of the machine was also less than earlier Fastracs. Power for the 1115 came from a six cylinder Perkins 115hp motor and there was still room behind the cab for a load-carrying platform.

Valmet Mezzo 6000 Series

Now part of the Sisu group, Valmet tractors have always been packed with novel and often advanced features. The Mezzo series of tractors was in many ways a continuation of the old Volvo BM designs, but featured the new ERGOCAB with the optional Twin-Trac reverse driving facility. Most were sold as four wheel drive tractors, but as can be seen by this 85hp 6300 model, they were also still available in two wheel drive form. The 115hp four cylinder 6800, was powered by a Sisu turbocharged and intercooled diesel engine and is shown in the more common four wheel drive layout. As is obvious from the pictures on this page, another unique feature of Valmet tractors was the choice of colours, which included shades of red, green, blue, yellow and white.

Massey Ferguson 6100 Series

Only two months into 1995 and Massey Ferguson, now owned by the American giant AGCO, replaced most of their tractor ranges in one fell swoop. The new 6100 Series formed the mid range models with four and six cylinder tractors up to 120hp. With 100hp on tap from its six cylinder Perkins motor, this 6160 has more than enough power for potato planting duties with this large KeyAg planter. The 32 x 32 Dynashift transmission was now available throughout the range, as was the Autotronic and Datatronic monitoring systems. The cab was new and featured a new layout for the hydraulic and pto controls and a revised dashboard. The gear lever layout however, would have been familiar to any driver of the outgoing 3000 and 3100 series machines.

Massey Ferguson 8100 Series

Massey Ferguson also launched a whole new range of larger tractors fitted with six cylinder power plants, Dynashift transmissions and the new Datatronic II. Two of the larger models are seen here, the 160hp 8140 and the flagship 200hp 8160. Valmet engines powered all these large tractors, including the 180hp 8150, while the 135hp 8110 to the 155hp 8130 had Perkins units. All were built in the French Beauvais factory.

Deutz Fahr Agrotron

Deutz Fahr stuck to their idea of sloping bonnets, and further enhanced it with brand new rounded cabs and curved lines when they launched the new Agrotron models in the autumn of 1995. The 4.95 illustrated working at the Grassland '96 event in Warwickshire, had 95hp available from its four cylinder engine. There were several tractors in the Agrotron range including larger six cylinder machines. Inside the futuristic cab all the tractors controls were cleverly colour-coded to make life easier for the driver, particularly if they were new to these tractors. But the biggest change was Deutz Fahr's ownership which had now passed to Italian manufacturer Same.

Case IH 4200

The ageing 95 Series tractors finally bowed out with the introduction of the new 3200 and 4200 machines. Mechanically they were very similar to the earlier models but they did now boast a newer low profile cab option, as well as the tried and tested XL cab. The gear controls were also repositioned and improved. In all, there were now six models, ranging from the 52hp three cylinder 3220, up to the 90hp four cylinder 4240, with the 4230 putting out 82 horses from its four pot motor. All were available with two or four wheel drive except for the top 4240 model, which was fitted with a four wheel drive front axle as standard.

New Holland 40 Series

Above and left: By 1996 the separate Ford and Fiat tractor ranges were becoming more and more integrated under the all-encompassing New Holland umbrella. The very popular 40 Series underwent a few changes, most notably it's colour scheme, but also including more useful upgrades such as extra hydraulic lift capacity. The Basildon built range was now also offered in Fiat terracotta as the S Series, not in the UK but in sensitive markets such as Italy where the Fiat name has always been more recognised than Ford. These changes gave the 40 Series models a breath of new life in their last few years of production.

Case IH Magnum 7200 Series

Left: The original Magnum 7100 Series was replaced in 1995 by the new 7200 models. Now with 188hp from its six cylinder motor, the 7220 was an impressive machine and by the time this picture was taken in 1996, its power had been increased once again – to 200hp! These American tractors were built with large arable farms in mind, with large amounts of power, traction and pure grunt. They also formed the vanguard in an ever-increasing power race, with rigid frame tractors taking the mantle from the mighty articulated machines, that had once ruled the roost in the 200-300hp bracket. The flagship 7250 model was now threatening this boundary with 267hp on tap!

Case IH Maxxum Pro 5100 Series

The successful Maxxum mid-range tractors saw their final incarnation with the Pro Series. Two examples are seen here, both at work on the potato crop, clearly showing the main feature of these new models – increased headroom for the driver, achieved by raising the cab's height by a few inches. Inside the cab the gear control layout had also changed, the sliding powershift control lever having been replaced by a new thumb switch, which now engaged the four powershift ratios. Still built in Germany, these tractors were proving their worth as a good all-rounder on farms throughout Europe.

Lamborghini Formula Limited/Same Antares Top

The Italian Same and Lamborghini mid-range models received a face lift in the mid 1990s and now appeared as 'Limited' in the Lamborghini Formula fold, or as 'Top' models in the Same Antares line-up. A 115hp Lamborghini Formula 115 Limited is shown busy with a Westmac JF RB300L round baler, while a 110hp Same Antares 110 Top is collecting maize from a self- propelled forager.

Valtra Valmet Mega 50 Series

Above: Still under Finnish control but with a change of management and name, Valmet tractors were now known as Valtra Valmet. Revised specifications included electronic controls and new transmissions.

Case IH CS Special

Below: Once again making use of the front linkage, this 110hp Case IH CS110 Special is equipped with front mounted Flexi-Coil complete with power harrow and pneumatic drill combination on the rear. This tractor was a direct result of the take-over of Steyr of Austria by Case International in 1996 and is basically a Steyr tractor painted into Case IH colours. It enabled the Case IH range to be expanded with higher specification models than those previously offered, the Steyr range being well ahead of many manufacturers in the field of electronics and transmission technology.

New Holland 35 Series/L Series

Above and left: 1996 saw the launch of the first New Holland badged tractors since the merger and they were still available in either Ford or Fiat colours, but the New Holland name was now much more prominent, as on the revised 40 Series tractors. Two different ranges were launched, one was a mid range six cylinder line up while the other was at the smaller end of the spectrum. The 35 and L Series were the latter and were produced in Italy, being the first Ford tractors to be built there. The 85hp 6635 was a more basic alternative to the 6640 and identical to the Fiat L85, except in colour. Biggest in the range was the 95hp 7635 - or L95 depending on your preference. A major feature of these new tractors was a lower profile version of the 40 Series cabin and the extremely short, sloping bonnet line.

New Holland 60 Series/ M Series

Right: The new six cylinder range from New Holland was anything but basic! These new machines, known as the 60 Series or M Series depending on parentage, were all made in Basildon and featured a wealth of electronic controls including electronic hydraulics and a new 18 x 16 Range Command powershift transmission. Starting from 100 horse (8160 – M100) the biggest in the range packed 160hp (8560 – M160) under its sleek, stylish bonnet.

John Deere 7010 Series

It was also in 1996 that John Deere announced an upgrade to the 7000 Series tractors. Now known as the 7010 range, these machines featured an improved specification over the outgoing models. Only two tractors now made up the range, the 7710 and the 7810. Front linkages were still popular as a means of using more of the tractor's available power, and this 175hp, six cylinder 7810 is shown at work with both front and rear mounted John Deere mowers.

New Holland Versatile 82 Series

Meanwhile, as rigid tractors gained in horsepower so did the giant artics from North America. Ford New Holland had bought the Versatile plant and its range of high horsepower artics back in 1987 and they remained in the New Holland line-up after the merger with Fiat. Soon the 80 Series was replaced by the improved 82 Series, including this monster 9682 with nearly 400hp under its enormous bonnet. Despite its impressive looks these tractors would remain a rare sight this side of the Atlantic.

New Holland 70 Series

Improvements were made to the 70 Series, also built in the Versatile factory alongside the giant artic leviathans. Several small improvements were made but the heart of the tractor was still the moveable control console next to the driver's seat, which housed the hydraulic spool valve controls, pto engagement, four wheel drive and diff lock switches as well as the single gear lever. The clever SuperSteer front axle option was still available, allowing a 65-degree turning angle.

JCB Fastrac 1000 Series

The 115hp Fastrac 1115 received a stable-mate with the introduction of the 1135. This tractor was built to the same smaller layout as the 1115, but featured extra horsepower in the shape of a 135hp six cylinder Perkins motor. These slightly more basic Fastracs were gaining in popularity and were seen as a brilliant compromise between speed, traction and manoeuvrability.

JCB brought out the clever 4WS four wheel steer system on the smaller Fastracs to further improve their turning circle, and this helped the tractors gain even more customers, especially those farmers looking for row crop tractors, the four wheel steering making them ideal for manoeuvring in-between growing crops and beds. Another model also appeared, the 125hp 1125 giving a comprehensive range of three six cylinder models to complement the larger Fastrac machines.

Case IH Steiger Quadtrac

The Steiger 9300 Series articulated high horsepower tractors were launched in 1996, under the auspices of Case International who had bought the American Steiger operation ten years before. Then, in 1997 a brand new Steiger tractor appeared – the Quadtrac. All four wheels were replaced by four rubber track units that gave this large machine a very small and light footprint for its size which enabled the tractor to turn on headlands without scuffing the soil, a traditional problem with conventional crawlers, even those fitted with rubber tracks. The 9350 was the first of the Quadtracs and soon proved popular in the UK with its six cylinder 310hp motor.

Claas Challenger

From 1997 the Caterpillar Challenger crawler range was sold in Europe under the Claas name and in Claas colours, after the two firms came to a marketing arrangement which also involved Claas Lexion combine harvesters being sold in certain parts of the world as Caterpillar machines. The new livery suited the machines well as can be seen by the new 255hp Challenger 55 ploughing with a nine furrow Gregoire Besson articulated plough.

Claas Challenger E Series

The larger Challengers also received the Claas treatment and had now moved on to the new generation of E Series machines. The 340hp 75E was now one of four models in the new range, the biggest being the 95E which, in tune with the horsepower race of the period, could push out over 400hp from its six cylinder electronically managed Caterpillar power plant.

New Holland TS

Top right: 1997 also saw new tractors appear from the Basildon factory in Essex. The New Holland TS Series was made up of three machines all with four cylinder PowerStar engines. Short, sharply sloping bonnets gave them a modern appearance and a long air intake pipe and cleaner bowl were mounted on the side of the cab front pillar. The cab itself was the same as fitted to the 40 and 60 Series tractors. Electronically controlled hydraulics were complemented by the Electroshift 16 forward by 16 reverse transmission. The 100hp TS110 was the biggest in the range and is seen here with a 3 metre Kuhn power harrow.

Massey Ferguson 4200 Series

Right and below: The long running 300 Series finally came to the end of the road in 1997 when it was replaced by the all new 4200 range. Still built in the Banner Lane factory in Coventry, the 4200 tractors featured a brand new cab and a more modern looking sloping bonnet. A new Perkins four cylinder 85hp engine is fitted in the 4245, while the bigger 4270 features a new six cylinder motor pumping out 110hp.

Case IH Magnum Pro 7200

Five high horsepower machines comprised the new Magnum Pro range from the 7210 to the massive 7250. The Silent Guardian II cab, powershift transmission and 8.3 litre engines completed the package, on what would prove to be the last incarnation of the original Magnum launched back in 1988.

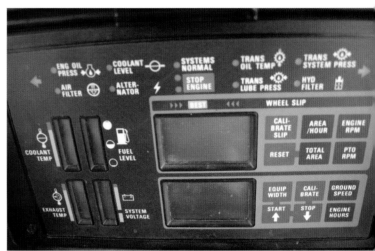

Massey Ferguson 6100 Series

Last to join the Massey Ferguson 6100 Series, the 6190 became the new flagship model with its six cylinder Perkins engine providing 130hp. As with all the 6100 and 8100 machines, the 6190 was built in Beauvais in France and featured the Dynashift transmission and Datatronic computer monitor. Not long ago, 130hp tractors would be part of the higher horsepower range offered by the major manufactures, but now machines like the 6190, offer more power in a lighter and more compact frame.

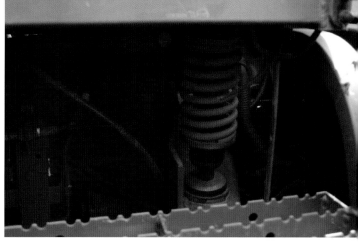

Renault Ares 600/700RZ

More activity in France saw Renault replace most of its mainstream tractor models in 1997. The new Ares range spanned 600 and 700 Series models and featured Deere six cylinder power plants, new cabs and a new transmission and back end, the last two being the result of the GIMA joint manufacturing agreement with Massey Ferguson. The 620 RZ had 120hp available while the bigger 710 packed 150hp and the range topping 735 pushed out 175hp. The new RZ cabs were fitted with the coiled spring suspension first seen on the TZ version in 1989.

Hurlimann Master

The Hurlimann tractor name has had a chequered history in the UK with only certain models being imported. The Swiss company for many years has been a part of the Same organisation, and Hurlimann tractor production was moved to Italy and were based on the same machines also sold as Lamborghini and Same tractors. For a while in the 1990s Hurlimann tractors enjoyed a resurgence of interest in Britain, with the largest H-6190 being one of the most popular models sold. Basically of the same design as it's stablemate brands, the 190hp six cylinder Hurlimann looks very imposing in its pale green livery. Soon models such as this would be phased out in favour of tractors based on the Deutz Fahr Agrotron range, as this design was adopted throughout the group.

Valtra Valmet Mega 50

New models from Finland included the six cylinder 8350, machines that carried on the Valmet trait of striking colour schemes. Customised paint colours were still available and these were enhanced by the addition of metallic colours of your choice and included a new light green livery following a marketing agreement with Claas. Inside the cab, electronics had overtaken the old levers and dials and a semi-powershift transmission completed the specification.

John Deere 6010

1997 was a good year for new tractor model introductions, boosted in no small measure by the launch of the John Deere 6010 Series. Externally the only difference from the outgoing 6000 Series was the brighter decals on the bonnet, but underneath there was more power from up-rated Deere engines and new transmission systems, as well as the addition of Triple Link Suspension on the front axle to boot! The 85hp four cylinder 6110 was only the second tractor in the range after the baby 75hp 6010.

The 6410 now boasted 105hp, five horses more than the 6400 it replaced. The smallest six cylinder in the range was now the 110hp 6510, with the 6610 rated at 115hp. A cheaper version of the 6010 range was also available and dubbed SE. The 6510 SE is shown as an example of these more basic specification tractors, external differences including the positioning of the exhaust on the side of the bonnet instead of its now usual home beside the cab pillar.

Lamborghini Formula

More electronics came to the Formula range complete with a new and very striking colour scheme. The new Multispeed transmission gave a three-speed change on the move at the touch of a button, which provided an amazing total of 72 x 72 gears in fully equipped form. Controls for the Multispeed were duplicated by being positioned on the gear lever itself, as well as on the Multifuction control handset, which is fitted on the armrest of the driving seat. Power comes from a water and oil cooled turbocharged 132hp six cylinder Lamborghini engine. A cab mounted exhaust stack was available as an option.

John Deere 8000T

Not content with just announcing the new 6010 tractors, John Deere also introduced the 8000T crawlers in 1997. These rubber tracked machines were based on the 8000 Series wheeled models, the only difference being below the patented full frame chassis, where the front and rear axles were replaced by two track units. Looking rather ungainly without front axles and with a big overhang, these crawlers were in fact well balanced, as the 8000 tractor design incorporated large engines mounted well forward on the chassis, giving excellent weight distribution, even with large fully mounted implements attached to the rear linkage. The biggest was the 260hp 8400T.

Case IH Maxxum MX

The original Maxxum models bowed out in 1997 in favour of the new MX Maxxums. It was not only the tractors that were new though, instead of being built in Germany the new Maxxums were now made in the Doncaster plant, making them the largest tractors ever to be built there. New cabs, revised transmissions, electronic hydraulic controls and new styling saw these tractors become a fitting replacement for the original Maxxum series. The model designations followed the tractor's horsepower closely, with the 110hp MX110 being the baby of the range, followed by the MX120 and MX135. Soon bigger versions were to appear, the biggest of which was the 170hp MX170 – compare that to the 125hp flagship of the old range.

Zetor 7341

Zetor tractors had always been the typical machine of the Eastern Bloc countries of Europe, basic but reliable designs that were cheap to produce and, just as importantly, easy to maintain. For many years their import into the UK was seen by many farmers as a means to purchase reliable machines at a bargain price, and therefore many Zetor, Belarus, IMT and Ursus machines found their way onto British farms, particularly livestock units.

Case IH CX

Above: Case IH's smaller tractor range was also revamped with the launch of the Doncaster built CX Series, which featured new cabs and improved gear and hydraulic systems. Their engines were also new, being built by Perkins. A complete break from Case IH tradition!

Deutz Fahr Agrotron MKII

This page and opposite bottom and bottom left: The Deutz
Fahr Agrotron range really started to come into its own
towards the end of the decade with tractors of well over 200
horses, but the smaller tractors also received a boost with the
introduction of the Agrotron MkII machines. The first Agrotrons
had proven troublesome in several areas and the new tractors
were redesigned to try and rectify these shortcomings. They
still retained their distinctive sharply sloping bonnets and
streamlined cabs though, as can be seen from this selection
ranging from the 135hp Agrotron 135 up to the 200hp 200 model,
which was the biggest of the conventional range.

When the two larger 230 and 260 Agrotrons appeared, boy were
they impressive! Once again the design made effective use of a
sloping bonnet and that rounded cab looked even more striking
perched up high on the top of these leviathans! The horsepower
once again matched the model designation, 230 and 260hp from
six cylinder water-cooled Deutz motors. Electronics featured
heavily inside the cab and all-round visibility was excellent
thanks to the side mounted cab and air intake, the latter's dry
element filter being housed down beside the left hand steps.
Cab and front axle suspension was available to provide a more
comfortable ride at the high road speed that these machines
were easily capable of.

JCB Fastrac 3100 Series

With new styling and 54 x 18 transmissions, the 3155 and 3185 Fastracs appeared in 1998. The 3155 had 155hp available from the Perkins six cylinder motor under its bonnet, while the flagship 3185 had 180hp from its Cummins unit. One 3185 is shown at the end of the production line at the JCB Landpower factory in Cheadle, Staffordshire were the Fastrac is assembled. Another is seen parked in the yard outside and is destined for Germany, complete with lower profile tyres and a higher ratio transmission that allows faster road speeds than in this country.

JCB Fastrac 2100 Series

The smaller Fastrac range also received a makeover with the new 2000 Series replacing the older models. The 2115 and 2135 were fairly straightforward replacements for the 1115 and 1135, but the 2150 was something new. It featured the chassis from the larger 3000 Series, mated to the cab and bonnet of the rest of the 2000 machines with a 148hp motor providing the grunt. The idea was to provide a higher horsepower Fastrac at a more affordable price.

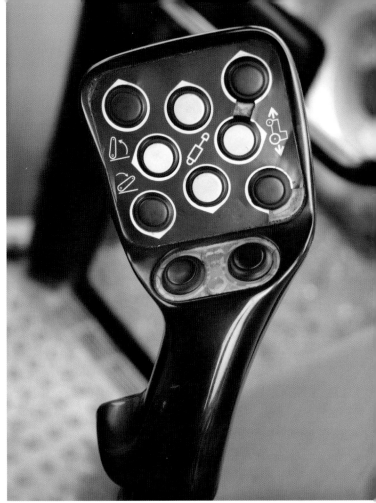

Case IH CS

Although still producing tractors in their own name, the range of Steyr built machines offered as part of the Case IH tractor line-up was still increasing. Many customers saw the Steyr tractors as offering a more upmarket tractor than the pure Case IH machines and there was certainly still a lot of sophisticated hardware up in the CS cabin, including most of the main tractor functions being controlled from the one stick.

Same Rubin

The Deutz Fahr influence became clear with the launch of the Same Rubin – sloping cab, rounded styling and that extraordinary cab design, features that looked even more striking in Same red livery. These two feature six cylinder liquid cooled diesels of 135 and 150hp. Standard gearbox is an electronically controlled powershift giving 18 x 18 gears over two ranges. An automatic powershift is optional.

Lamborghini Champion/Runner

Lamborghini's version of the Same Rubin kept the formula racing car theme of earlier models as they were dubbed Champions. The new styling and silver paint scheme contrived to make these tractors look very breathtaking indeed! Underneath the skin the Lamborghini engine made use of the companies new RISE (Resonance Intake System Engine) technology with 18 valves - three valves per cylinder.

Front axle and cab suspension were available as an option and control of the tractor was through a multi function control lever mounted on an armrest console. The smaller end of the market was also catered for by the tiny Runner tractor range aimed at horticultural, municipal and vineyard operators and comprised three models from 25 to 40hp, the Runner 350 being the middle of the range at 35 horses.

New Holland TS

It took a year or so after the launch of the original four cylinder TS series tractors from New Holland before they were joined by a new six cylinder flagship – the TS115. Replacing the long running 7840 model, the TS115 still managed to pack its extra horsepower under a short, sloping bonnet. Inside, the cab was familiar to any TS user and included the option of the ElectroShift 16 x 16 transmission, although the more basic mechanical shift Dual Power was also still available.

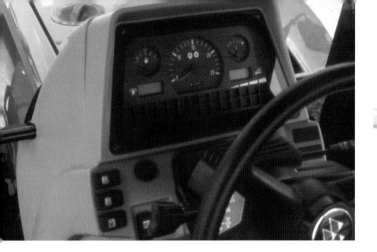

Massey Ferguson 6200

New, sleeker styling personified the new 6200 Massey Ferguson tractors, but they also featured new Perkins engines and the Datatronic II tractor monitoring computer system. The range spanned models from the 100hp 6260 up to the largest, the 140hp 6290, all with six cylinder motors. The 130hp 6280 shown here, was on demonstration at Grassland '99. Dynashift transmission was still fitted giving 32 x 32 speeds.

Case IH Magnum MX

The long serving Case IH Magnum 7200 Series, finally bowed out in 1999 in favour of an all new American built tractor range. These high horsepower monsters feature a longer wheelbase, forward mounted engine to provide better balance when using large heavy implements, and an all-new cab with a huge amount of glass area. These impressive machines were led by the range topping MX285, with a maximum of 311hp from its six cylinder intercooled power plant, driving through an 18 x 4 full powershift transmission, controlled by a rocker switch on the chrome effect hand throttle, positioned on the arm rest console.

New Holland TNS

Right: Designed for the smaller farm, orchards and vineyards the TNS tractors are compact, powerful and are available with an option fitted to some of the largest New Holland tractors. This is the SuperSteer front axle, which allows a much tighter turning circle than the conventional version. TNS machines like this TN75S, are fitted with a scaled down version of the system first seen on the 70 Series tractors.

New Holland TV

Above: This tractor was designed and built by Versatile in Canada and was the end product of many years of development. The earlier versions were very popular in North America but much less so in Europe, so with the Versatile range now under New Holland ownership, a new version of this bi-directional tractor appeared based around the 60 Series engine and styling. Like the previous Versatile machines it was articulated, had equal size wheels and a hydrostatic transmission, which made it an ideal machine for loader work such as filling the silage clamp, especially with 140hp on tap! Despite a few sales, particularly into niche markets such as peat harvesting and contracting, the TV 140 eventually became lost amongst the upheaval of the forthcoming Case IH and New Holland merger.

Doppstadt Trac

When Mercedes-Benz stopped manufacture of the MB Trac range in favour of the Unimog, a large gap in the systems tractor market was left. JCB did a good job of filling it with the Fastrac, but many people still missed the original MB Trac, leading to German firm Doppstadt producing modernised versions of the lime green classic. With 160hp the Trac 160 was one of a range of tractors of up to 200hp featuring new cabs with a powershift gearbox, air brakes, electronic controls and a new yellow and black livery, while still earning the right to wear the famous Merc badge by virtue of being powered by six cylinder Mercedes-Benz diesels.

Fendt Vario 700 Series

Left and below left: The Vario stepless transmission was the first such technology to be included in a production tractor when it appeared in the Fendt 900 Series flagship models. Soon it would filter down to smaller machines built by this German company, including the new 700 Series tractors that sported front axle and cab suspension, an array of electronic controls and bonnet styling by Porsche. The Vario system gives the operator infinite speeds from 0-50kph at any given engine speed and is one of the most important technological advances in tractor design in recent years.

Massey Ferguson 8200 Series

Opposite and below: Massey Ferguson, like Fendt, is part of the giant AGCO conglomerate, but at this stage the two brands were operating completely independently of each other. The larger end of the power bracket was catered for by the 8200 Series that replaced the older 8100 range. Changes were not great but included revised bonnet styling, Datatronic II and the new PowerControl system that included a single lever mounted on the armrest console along with hydraulic controls.

Deutz-Fahr Agrotron MKII

The Agrotron four and six cylinder models continued their development with the introduction of the new and improved MKII versions. Generally much the same as the original machines, these tractors kept their distinctive sloping bonnets and rounded cabs, but underneath several improvements were made to iron out some of the problems encountered with the first generation machines, including a revamp of the operating controls inside the cab. Other features introduced on the Mk II included the option of powershift transmissions and front axle and cab suspension.

Claas Xerion

Another break from the norm was the large machine that represented German Claas' first entry into the tractor market on its own account. But the Xerion was far from an ordinary tractor, not only were three models from 250 (like the 2500 shown) to 350hp available, but they all featured a new stepless transmission, four equal size wheels with different steering modes and a load platform at the rear. The really outstanding feature though was the moveable cab. This was designed so that it could be positioned in one of four different layouts so that various harvesting machinery could be wrapped around the tractor, turning it into a self-propelled potato, sugar beet harvester or even into a forage harvester or combine. The next day all this could be removed and the Xerion could return to plough the fields it had just harvested. Perhaps this would be the shape of modern tractors in the 21st century?

Renault Atles

With the launch of the two Atles models, Renault now had a presence in the elite high horsepower sector. These big impressive looking machines were completely new, although they did take some of their design cues from the existing Ares models. Deutz six cylinder motors powered both the 215hp 925RZ and the 240hp 935RZ through state of the art transmission and electronic systems. Cab and front axle suspension completed the powerful package. This 935RZ was on test in Norfolk, complete with six furrow Rabe slatted mouldboard plough and shows off the radical new styling of the Atles range. And yes Stephen did like it!

Case IH CX

Above: Case IH always liked to offer special promotional versions of its tractors over the years. This is the Landsman Special variant of the 100hp four cylinder CX 100 built in Doncaster. As you can see the styling cues are taken from the larger Maxxum MX range, particularly the rounded nose cone and outward cab design.

Case IH Maxxum MX Extra

Below: A special promotion on the Case IH MX Maxxum, led to the MX135 Extra based on the standard 135hp model, but with a completely red painted chassis, wheel centres and back end, as well as extra worklights mounted on top of the cab roof and other usually optional extras fitted as standard. Although it was not known at the time, the red chassis would be an indication of things to come!

New Holland TM

New Holland replaced the 60 Series tractors with the TM range. Outwardly they looked basically the same, except for the decals, but this was far from the full story. These new tractors came with an impressive range of options throughout the four model range, including the SuperSteer front axle brought down from the 70 Series. Alternatively the purchaser could choose the TerraGlide suspended front axle instead. The TM range spanned models from the baby 115hp TM115 to the range topping 165hp TM165. The TM135 had 135hp under the sleek hood while the TM150 produced 150hp.

The transmission systems were much the same as the outgoing 60 Series. Later the TM165 Ultra appeared, so called because it was the standard 165hp model, now equipped with the TerraGlide front axle suspension, as well as the new cab suspension featuring two coil springs mounted at the rear.

97

Case IH CVX

Fendt were the first company to produce a constantly variable transmission production tractor with the Vario, but Steyr were not far behind with their own version, which, once the company had been taken over by Case IH, resulted in these tractors reaching a wider audience. As Case IH machines, they were known as the CVX range and spanned several models from the 130hp CVX130 up to the 170hp CVX170, all with six cylinder engines and the 'gearless' transmission. Styling was similar to earlier Steyr models and, of course, the previous CS Case IH tractors. The CVX machines though, had a new bonnet design which gave them a more menacing appearance than the earlier tractors, as well as the wishbone design front axle suspension system, the same type as used on contemporary MX Maxxum models.

Lamborghini Premium

The mid-range Premium tractors from Lamborghini were extended into the higher horsepower market with the introduction of the Premium 1300. With 132hp, six cylinders and the striking silver paint job, these machines looked very modern, even though the cab design was still as first used back in the 1990s. This one has plenty of power to spare hauling a trailer full of potato boxes beside a Reekie Cleanflow 2000 harvester, the rear view of which clearly shows the roof mounted cab air filters. The other tractor in the range was the 110hp Premium 1100.

John Deere 6020 Series

John Deere launched an impressive range of new tractor models in 2001. The 6020 Series took over from the 6010 range and although they were based on the previous models, new engines, transmission options and much more 'in your face' styling made them seem much fresher. A new cab suspension system called HCS (Hydraulic Cab Suspension), which allowed 100mm of travel, joined the TLS II front axle 'buffering' system. Still using Deere & Co.'s patented full frame design, the 6020 models spanned tractors from the 80hp 6120 up to the 6920S using both four and six cylinder Deere power plants. The 125hp 6620 features a six pot and is fitted with the PowrQuad Plus transmission which gives four powershift speeds in six gear ranges, with all the controls mounted on the neat console to the drivers right and a fully adjusted steering wheel. At the back of the tractor, extra worklights are provided as are external hydraulic controls mounted in the left hand side mudguard. The 135hp 6820 is further up the power scale but keeps the family looks whilst the 6920S is the top of the range model, with 160hp available at maximum power, ten horses more than the 6920 model that comes in at 150 horses.

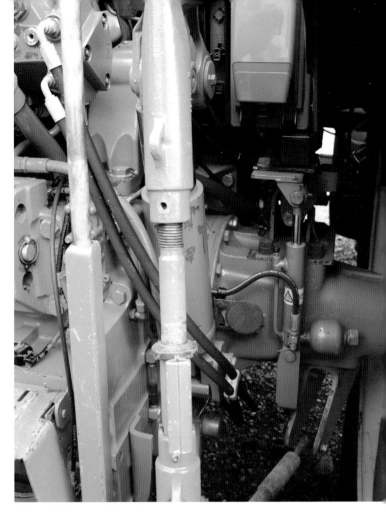

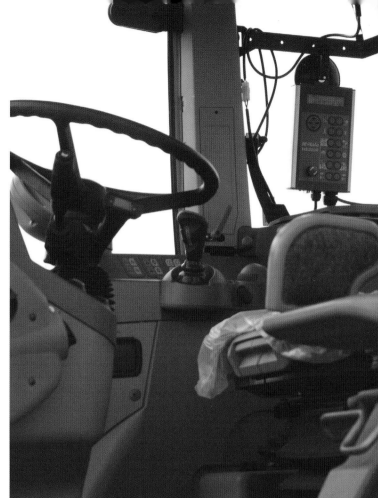

Fendt Vario

Fendt continued to offer more of its tractor range with the Vario transmission in 2001, especially with the launch of smaller four cylinder machines like the 128hp 412, as well as much bigger tractors like the 195hp 818. Both also kept with the new styling first seen in 1999 on the 700 Series Varios. Having started the constantly variable transmission concept, Fendt were determined to make the best possible use of the technology throughout its tractor range.

Massey Ferguson 8200 Xtra

The 8200 models received a facelift with the introduction of the Xtra range. With enhanced specifications these machines were an attempt to regain the flagging sales of the Massey Ferguson stable. The 8240 was middle of the range and is seen at work with a five furrow Dowdeswell plough, while the original model, the 8280 Xtra, is seen on display at an agricultural show.

Renault Ares II

The new, improved Renault Ares II tractors offered several new improvements in the cab, including a repositioned gear lever at a better angle for the operator, a new button on the back of the gear lever which acted as a clutch, a new seat and automatic speed matching. From the four cylinder 500 series, the 100hp 556RX was a powerful tractor for its size and easily capable of handling a two row Reekie potato harvester. The six cylinder 600 series machines spanned several models including the 100hp 616RZ base model, which like the rest of the range is available without cab suspension as the RX version, or with it as the RZ. The 636RZ comes in at 125hp from its Deere Power Systems engine, while the 656RZ fills out the range with 145hp available.

Deutz Fahr TTV

Above: Same Deutz Fahr's first constantly variable transmission first appeared in 2001 with a range of different horsepower. The biggest was the 160hp TTV1160 shown here on demonstration in 2002 with a combination drill. With these new machines Deutz Fahr also launched a new colour scheme with a black band wrapping itself round the bonnet to relieve the expanse of previously green paintwork.

Deutz Fahr Agrotron MK3

Right: Gradually new generation MK3 Deutz Fahr Agrotron tractors appeared on the scene during the early years of the 21st century. The range would eventually span models from the Agrotron 90 up to the mighty Agrotron 250. Two mid range examples are shown here, the 150 and 165 MK3 tractors with horsepower approximating that of the model number.

McCormick MC

Above: The new McCormick 115hp MC115, was designed to fit into the range as a four cylinder alternative to the six cylinder MTX120 and packed a good deal of power under its small bonnet

McCormick MTX

Below: As a result of the merger of New Holland and Case IH, it was necessary for Case IH to sell its Doncaster factory and the line of tractors made there. The result was the birth of a new company with an old name - McCormick, a company formed by the Italian owners of Landini. At first the newly born firm carried on producing revamped models based on the MX Maxxum and CX tractors designed by Case, but it did not take long before major changes were made to differentiate the new tractors. The colour scheme immediately set them apart and the MX tractors became the MTX range, with examples like this 147hp MTX140 and flagship MTX175 with 176hp under the bonnet. New transmission systems are among the new features of these tractors, including a red chassis!

John Deere 8020/8020T

Opposite: When John Deere gave the 8010 series the '20' treatment, they certainly pulled out all the stops in the 'looking mean' department. They also upped the power game with a new flagship model, the 295hp 8520. As before, these tractors were available with wheels or rubber tracks, as well as a whole host of sophisticated features from the Independent Link Suspension on the front axle, to the automatic driving system which allows the driver to sit back as the tractor drives itself across the field in a dead straight line, all thanks to GPS technology.

John Deere 9020T

Left and below: John Deere's 20 spree didn't stop there though, indeed it also spread even higher up the horsepower scale to the giant 9020 articulated pivot steer models. Also available as rubber tracked crawlers, the latter are much more common in the UK than the wheeled equivalents and are still quite an awesome sight. Two models are shown here, the 375hp 9320T, which has been busy with a Vaderstad Rexius cultivator and the then biggest tractor in the line-up, the mighty 9420T, pulling a very large Amazone cultivator drill while on demonstration in Norfolk. This has since been ousted by the even bigger 9520 which at 500hp, is the biggest ever tractor built by Deere & Co – to date at least!

New Holland TM

Revised decals brightened up the New Holland TM Series in 2002, but the range was just as comprehensive as before, with examples like the 124hp TM120 and 140hp TM140 seen here with a combination drill. Bigger versions included the TM155 shown collecting sugar beet from an Agrifac Big Six self-propelled harvester. The real big guys were the 194hp TM190 and the 177hp TM175, noticeable by their bigger physical size as well as their extra horses.

Case IH Maxxum MXM

With the loss of the Doncaster built Maxxum MX tractors there was a gaping hole left in the Case tractor range. The answer was to produce a Case version of the New Holland TM tractors and this worked very successfully. The 124hp New Holland TM120, metamorphosed into the Case IH Maxxum MXM120 as shown here at work with a TIM three-row sugar beet harvester. With an 18 x 12 powershift transmission (31 x 24 in the case of this particular machine as it is fitted with a creeper box), electronic control of all the major functions and external hydraulic buttons, this tractor would still be familiar to any driver used to Case machines, most noticeably with the chrome gear selector, making it totally different to the lever used on the blue TM machines. If a more basic specification was required, the Synchro box with the basic 12 x 6 speeds and mechanical control of the hydraulic system, complete with analogue dashboard was available.

Of course, the rest of the TM range was emulated as red Case IH tractors, like the MXM130 and the bigger MXM175, with the MXM190 topping out the range with a full power-shift transmission, as with the blue models. All were built on the same production line at the Basildon factory in Essex.

Valtra S Series

Right: Changes were afoot at the Finnish headquarters however, and a shortening of the name to Valtra coincided with the start of a complete revamp of all the models in the range. New flagship models were launched in the shape of the all-new S Series 230 and 260 models, with very distinctive styling, new engines, new transmissions and a radically new cab. By 2005 the range comprised only one model, the big S280 which housed a throbbing 280hp six cylinder Sisu diesel. Another benefit of the new tractors, and something that Valtra and its predecessors have offered for a long time, is the reverse drive function which allows the tractor to be driven as easily in forward or reverse by just swivelling the seat, ideal for jobs like this with a huge set of Kuhn mowers.

Valtra Valmet Mega 50

Below and right: Back in the mid-1990s, Valmet were the first to manufacture a production tractor which could produce more horsepower from the pto on demand, using electronic engine fuelling to achieve this. Today, virtually every large tractor and some not so large, are equipped with this facility. When the company was renamed as Valtra Valmet, the top model in the range was also fitted with this system and here it is, the 8950. With lots of horsepower available under its long snout, the addition of intercooling, as proudly proclaimed on the bonnet side, allowed even more efficient production of raw power.

Case IH JXU

Despite the introduction of the MXM range, smaller tractors were also needed to bring the Case IH product line up to date, and new introductions included the JXU range like this JX90U seen at an agricultural show.

Case IH STX

At the top end, Case IH still had what was in many ways the jewel in its crown, the Steiger range of high horsepower tractors. Designed as articulated pivot steer four wheel drive machines, they were also available as the unique Quadtrac and the largest was the 450hp STX450. Because New Holland was required to sell its Verasatile brand and factory, blue versions of the STX have appeared as New Holland TJ tractors in North America and other parts of the world.

New Holland TG

With the loss of the Versatile facilities, New Holland also lost the popular 70 Series tractors. The solution to the problem was the introduction of the very striking looking TG series machines, based on the earlier Case IH Magnum MX platform but with a much shorter bonnet giving a more stubby and workmanlike appearance. Biggest of all was the TG285 with 311hp on tap from its six cylinder 8.3 litre turbocharged and intercooled engine. With a very 'in your face' front end you certainly knew when the TG was on the scene!

Case IH Magnum MX

Above: With the new TG Series appearing, the Magnum MX range received some minor tweaking but remained basically as before. However, not many of the 311hp MX285 tractors could have found themselves undertaking this task; filling a silage clamp. Mind you, that is a rather large front mounted buckrake!

John Deere 6020 SE

Below: A more basic version of the John Deere 6020 appeared dubbed the SE range. The new tractors looked identical to the Premium 6020s from the outside, the only main giveaway being the bonnet mounted exhaust stack. These tractors featured far fewer electronics, with mechanical controls taking prominence.

Valtra T Series

The T Series from Valtra was launched at the same time as the S series and filled the gap below the two high horse-power models. The 120hp six cylinder Sisu powered T120, was on demonstration with a Saunders cultivator and is fitted out to a high specification with powershift transmission and electronic controls. The pale green metallic colour scheme was just one of the colours on offer, others being red and blue. The company is still proud of the fact that all its tractors are made to order and to the customer's exact requirements, right down to the preferred colour.

Massey Ferguson 6400 Series

Above: The Massey Ferguson 6200 range was replaced in 2003 by the new 6400 tractors. Originally only six cylinder models were available but these were soon joined by four cylinder variants. The 6465 has 130hp at its disposal at maximum load from a six cylinder Perkins motor, and still features the ever popular Dynashift 32 x 32 transmission. With the launch of these new models, AGCO declared that it was prepared to invest in the Massey Ferguson brand after a few years of declining sales, a position made all the more obvious by the more advance features of the 7400 series launched at the same time.

Massey Ferguson 7400 Series

Right: The Massey Ferguson 7400 series was much more radical and made use of Fendt technology, including the Vario stepless transmission and control computer. Dubbed the Dyna VT this gave Massey Ferguson one of the leading constantly variable transmissions and an instant leap into the big league of tractor sophistication. Red and grey was back! The 7490 provided 170hp from its Sisu diesel with a further power boast giving 180hp maximum output.

117

Zetor Forterra

Opposite Top: The Zetor range has been radically modernised of late to keep up with Western tractor trends, and the new sloping bonnets of the Forterra range and more horsepower from six cylinder engines have helped to keep the popularity of this Eastern European brand into the 21st century. The biggest in the range is the 11741 with a 120hp 6 cylinder Lamborghini engine under the sleek hood, which drives through a 24 x 18 three-speed powershift transmission giving a top speed of 40 Kph.

McCormick MTX

Opposite Bottom: McCormick uprated the MTX range in 2003 with extra power for most models. The 152hp MTX150 replaced the MTX140 and this example is seen with a Richard Western side delivery manure spreader. The extra power was a bonus of the new Tier II EEA engines now fitted to the MTX range.

Challenger MT Series

This page: Caterpillar's new range of rubber-tracked crawlers had barely been launched when the whole operation was sold to AGCO. This meant that the Claas badged machines in Europe would no longer exist, as AGCO made the Challenger brand into a completely new entity, even selling Massey Ferguson sourced wheeled tractors in Challenger colours alongside the crawlers in certain world markets. The new Challenger MT series was made up of two ranges, the 255hp MT765 being the biggest of the smaller models, while the biggest of all was the mighty 500hp MT865. New from the ground up these machines featured new cabs, engines and transmission systems and up in the cab there was a more obvious use of electronics including a computer monitor attached to the armrest console. Here we have a MT765 ploughing in stubble while a 380hp MT845 gets to grips with a 6m Kuhn power harrow.

McCormick MC Power6

Above: First making an appearance at the 2002 Smithfield Show, the new McCormick 115hp MC120 and 132hp MC135 were new six cylinder Doncaster built tractors. The Power 6 designation referred to the fact that they were an alternative to existing four cylinder machines.

McCormick MTX

Left: The flagship McCormick MTX185, was eventually replaced as the largest model by the new MTX200 with 204 horses available. This was now the largest tractor ever built at the Doncaster factory and was McCormick's first foray into the league of high horsepower machines.

McCormick CX Xtrashift

Below: Launched in 2003, the Xtrashift transmission gave the McCormick CX series tractors an extra edge. A thumb switch on the main gear lever changed between four powershift ranges on the move. Externally the tractors remained unchanged.

Deutz Fahr Agrotron

Above: With Italian owners Same now fully in the driving seat, new Deutz Fahr Agrotrons began to appear with increasing frequency. The 210 featured the TTV type styling and presage a complete revamp of the range, from the Agrotron 130 model up to the new 235 and 250 tractors.

Massey Ferguson 5400 Series

Right: The Massey Ferguson 5400 series was launched in the autumn of 2003 and comprised a wide range of Perkins powered four cylinder tractors, including the sloping bonnet 90hp 5445 and the larger 115hp 5460 with standard bonnet lines. The sloping bonnet, or high visibility model carried on a tradition of curved bonnet models first seen on the 3065HV version back in the early 1990s. This one is also seen with the lower roof cab, designed with the stock farmer's low buildings in mind. All the 5400 series tractors are built in the Beauvais factory in France.

New Holland TSA

The winter of 2003 saw the arrival of a completely new range of New Holland tractors, featuring brand new Horizon cabs and styling inherited from the big TG series. Both four and six cylinder tractors from 101 to 136hp made up the TSA range, with the baby TS100A and TS110A being four cylinder models, while the TS135A was the flagship six cylinder tractor.

Case IH Maxxum MXU

The launch of the New Holland TSA series also resulted in the introduction of the Case IH Maxxum MXU range, based on the same common platform design and featuring the new cabs, transmissions and engines. The styling though, was different, carrying on the tradition of the older Maxxum models. Horse power ratings were exactly the same as the New Holland machines and the range was also available in the Austrian Steyr colours as the Profi range, although all the tractors were actually built in Basildon, Essex.

Case IH CVX

New styling, although not radically so, was also the order of the day for the new Steyr based and Austrian built Case IH CVX range. Several models were built including the 1145 145hp version, and the biggest of the lot, the CVX1190, with 190hp under the mean looking bonnet from a Sisu six cylinder power plant. At the heart of the machine was the constantly variable transmission system, giving unlimited and smooth forward and reverse speeds.

JCB Fastrac

A change of decals and curvier bonnet lines announced the arrival of a new and more powerful JCB Fastrac flagship model. Now with 200hp pumping out of its Cummins QSB engine, the new 3220 was the biggest Fastrac to date but it was very much an evolution of the Fastrac design rather than a revolution, as under the new styling it was the same machine as the older 3185, albeit more powerful. Inside the cab though, changes were more noticeable with a new design of control binnacle, featuring more electronic controls including timed spool valves.

Fendt Vario 900 Series

The mighty Fendt Vario 924 was usurped as the firms largest model with the arrival of the Vario 930, launched in Britain in 2003. This 300hp machine was very similar to the 924, and of course, included the Vario constantly variable transmission, which was the first production transmission of this type in the world. The new 930 is an impressive beast, complete with long snout and wrap round radiator, making a fitting flagship to this German firms line up.

John Deere 7020 Series

A new type of Deere began running in 2003. The impressive looking 7020 series spanned three models, the 182hp 7720, 197hp 7820 and 215hp 7920 fitting in between the 6920S and the 8120 models. These tractors new aggressive styling left everybody with the impression that these machines meant business, and with the option of John Deere's new CVT transmission which they called the Infinitely Variable Transmission or IVT, they certainly had the technology to go with their distinctive looks. High powered but versatile machines, these tractors are equally at home with large front and rear mounted mower conditioners or hauling wheat away from the combine in large trailers, jobs all made easier by the IVT transmission.

JCB Fastrac

More new-look JCB Fastracs soon appeared. The 148hp 2140 was now the sole representative of the smaller series machines and was still available with four wheel steer. The bigger 3170 was now the baby in the larger range with 170hp squeezed out of its six cylinder motor. All the new Fastracs are powered by Cummins power plants.

Landini Vision

Opposite top: The Italian built Landini tractor range was swelled by a new 105hp mid-ranger with the introduction of the Perkins powered Vision 105, seen here using Reco Fella grassland equipment.

Landini Legend

Bigger Landini tractors are also still available with the new generation of Legend machines featuring much more use of the latest in sophisticated electronics. Several transmission options are topped off by the offer of a remarkable 108 x 36 gears, these are made up by a combination of Top-Tronic, Speed Six and creeper gearboxes. The 135 TDI model has a maximum power of 134hp, the 145 comes out at 145hp and the range topping 185 with 183hp from Perkins 6 cylinder TierII electronic fuel injected motors. Even larger Landini tractors are also offered, the Starlander range being built by Buhler Industries of Canada and based on the old Ford 70 Series tractors.

McCormick ZTX

This mighty machine represents the largest tractor range ever built in the old International Harvester factory in Doncaster. The 260hp Cummins powered McCormick ZTX260 joins the 230hp ZTX230 and the largest, the ZTX280, in a new range of high-horsepower tractors launched by the firm in 2004, making an impressive sight with their brand new cab and distinctive exterior styling. A new 18 x 8 full powershift transmission featuring a speed matching facility, pre-programmable start off gears as well as a multi gear shift ability, is fitted as standard.

Valtra M Series

Right: Valtra, now a part of AGCO, soon went about the task of replacing all its tractor range with new models based very much on the styling of the S series launched in 2002. The four model M series represents the four cylinder range from 120hp to 150hp, and includes a 36 x 36 transmission and also comes with a couple of very interesting derivatives....

Valtra XM

Right and below: And here's one of them, the 130hp XM130. These tractors can literally bend round corners and are based on earlier tractors designed for forestry work. The cab is actually mounted behind a pivot point so that the bonnet and cab section are separate and the whole tractor can articulate, this makes it extremely useful for working with front loaders in the confined spaces of a stockyard or in narrow buildings.

Claas Celtis

Above: After the German harvesting machinery firm Claas bought the tractor operations from French based Renault, it was only a matter of time before the familiar orange paintwork gave way to the red and green worn by a whole host of German built machinery. From 2004 the whole Renault range was available in Britain in Claas colours and the smaller Celtis machines were no exception. When Renault first launched these four cylinder Deere engine tractors, they were the first to receive new front end treatment, which would eventually set the pattern for bigger tractors in the range. The Celtis machines are fitted with a low roofline, ideal for the livestock farmer.

Claas Ares

Right: The bigger four and six cylinder Ares 500, 600 and 800 series tractors also received the Claas treatment and certainly stand out in their new clothes. Otherwise though, the tractors are really identical to the Renault badged machines before them, but it's amazing how a change of colour can make all the difference!

Claas Atles

The range topping Atles models, now proudly displaying their Claas identity, still make an impressive sight whatever task they are carrying out and have been revamped only slightly since the introduction of the original Atles range in 2001. Still powered by Deutz watercooled motors, the flagship Atles 936 pumps out 253hp and a maximum torque of 1050Nm at 1500rpm. The smaller 926 has 232hp available.

New Holland TVT

With Case IH proving very successful with it's Steyr built CVX range, it was not long before the blue New Holland line-up would benefit from the clever constantly variable transmission offered by these tractors. Although built on the same Austrian production line as the Case IH and Steyr machines, the New Holland TVT tractors have been fitted out with styling that keeps them in the same family as the TG and TSA ranges, and don't they look good! Biggest in the range is the 193hp, six cylinder TVT190 with power coming from Sisu six cylinder diesel engines. The smallest is the TVT135 pumping out 139hp while the TVT155 produces 159hp.

Massey Ferguson

AGCO owned Massey Ferguson, revamped the higher horsepower bracket with the launch of the impressive looking 8400 Series. Built in the same factory as the smaller tractors in the MF range, these new machines certainly look the part, their new styling helping to make them look much more workmanlike than the outgoing 8200 Series tractors. Equipped with six cylinder Sisu motors, the range encompassed four models from the 8450 with a maximum output of 235hp, to the flagship 8480 with 315 horses available under the bonnet at maximum power from its 8.4 litre engine. Quadlink front axle suspension, cab suspension, Dyna VT constantly variable transmission and Datatronic III with full colour console mounted monitor, are just a few of the advanced features available as standard on these top end machines.

New Holland TSA

Left: 2005 saw New Holland launch a new look decal for the bonnets of their blue tractor ranges. The old Fiatagri logo now took on yet another lease of life in a bright yellow and blue guise and the end result was to brighten up the tractor range considerably. Largest of the TSA range, the TS135A is seen here with a set of Kuhn front and rear mounted mowers.

New Holland TM

Left and below: The new corporate image suited the TM tractors too. The TM175 and TM190 were still the largest in the range, and although looking small compared to the larger TG tractors, were still very powerful machines. The cab, basically of the same structure as launched on the 40 Series back in 1991, does not look its age, probably due to the fact that these tractors are brim full of electronic driving aids and other gizmos.

Case IH MXM Pro

Right: The Case IH version of the TM range entered the twilight of its life with the addition of the Pro decal, just as the older Maxxum had done back in the 90s. Biggest is still the MXM190 with 194hp, complete with power boost to 229 horses, and comes with two gearbox options, either 19 x 6 economy full powershift which gives a top speed of 40kph, or the 19 x 6 full powershift 50kph box which can also be specified with the option of a 29 x 12 creeper box. The 155hp MXM155 comes complete with an 18 x 6 six-speed powershift transmission or the 18 x 6 full powershift. Smallest in the range is the 124hp MXM120 Pro.

Case IH Steiger STX Quadtrac

Right and below: Monster tractors keep on getting bigger, and more popular! With 500hp under its large hood, the STX500 Quadtrac weighs in at 24129kg total weight, yet still manages to tread lightly. Drive from the 15 litre Cummins diesel is taken through a 16 x 2 powershift gearbox, the fuel tank has a maximum capacity of 1138 litres with an optimum fuel consumption of 69 litres per hour! This particular example is actually the 50,000th Steiger tractor produced in North America.

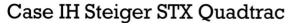

Landini Powerfarm

Above: Landini tractors now have a larger presence in the UK than ever before. The five model Powerfarm series encompasses a power range from 58 to 98hp, with the 75 model offering 68hp at maximum power from its four cylinder un-blown Perkins motor. Gear options include a 12 x 12 mechanical box or a 32 x 16 splitter including creeper gears. The cab, called TotalView, features air conditioning and is available in two versions, Top and Techno.

Deutz Fahr Agrotron

Left and opposite: With Same Deutz Fahr continuing to develop the common platform principle, the various makes included in the Italian stable keep on becoming more and more integrated, sharing many different components. These mid-range models shown encompass 118 to 170hp with smaller and larger Agrotrons making up a very comprehensive range. Four stage powershift transmission, front axle and cab suspension and pneumatic seat endeavour to make the operator as comfortable as possible.

Merlo Multifarmer

With farm incomes continually under pressure today, machinery has to be ever more efficient and versatile. Italian materials handler firm, Merlo, decided to make their agricultural telehandlers even more handy by fitting them with a three point linkage and pto, the result being called the Multifarmer, to differentiate it from the more standard telehandler called the Turbofarmer. Primarily aimed at livestock farmers who currently use tractor loader combinations, the Multifarmer offers all the advantages of a telehandler, such as four wheel drive, different steering modes and of course the telescopic boom, while also being able to go out in the field and pull a four furrow reversible plough.

It's real versatility was demonstrated at the Grassland 2006 demonstration in Warwickshire, where a Multifarmer was used to mow the grass, followed by a second machine that picked up the crop with a JF forage harvester, while a third Multifarmer hooked up to the full trailer and carted the whole lot to the clamp, where a Turbofarmer clamped and rolled the grass, the whole operation being performed without a single tractor! Four models are available in the Multifarmer range all being powered by a Deutz four cylinder turbo with aftercooler producing 115hp. Rear lift capacity is 4300kg and the pto can operate at 540 and 1000rpm. Inside the side-mounted cab a screen to the driver's right, called the Merlin Digital Control system, displays the operation of all the machines functions giving complete electronic control. A two speed hydrostatic transmission, transmits the power and allows the machine to travel at up to 40kph.

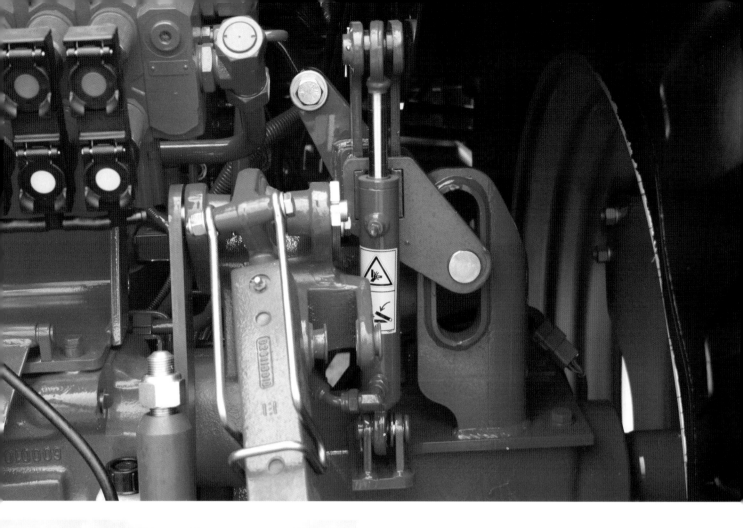

McCormick XTX

With the large ZTX models occupying the top slot, McCormick introduced slightly smaller versions in 2005 and dubbed them the XTX series. Replacing the top models of the MTX range and filling the gap before the mighty ZTX, these tractors featured a new cab design and brand new 32-speed transmission. The new gearbox gives eight powershift gears in four ranges operated by a console-mounted gearlever that also doubles up as a rear linkage controller. Three models make up the range with maximum power from 198 to 228hp from new Cummins QSB six cylinder 6.7 litre motors. Both the front axle and cab can be fitted with suspension systems to ease the ride, the front axle suspension being of the wishbone type. The XTX185 and 200 models shown here, were both on display at the Grassland 2005 event – their first public working demonstration.

Claas Xerion

Claas unveiled a new Xerion in 2005, replacing the slow selling three model range with a single model available in three different forms. Now with a 335hp 8.8 litre Caterpillar six cylinder turbocharged engine, and a ZF infinitely variable CVT transmission which gives a top speed (in both directions) of 50kph. The Xerion 3300 System version has a rotating cab that can be placed in two different positions, either the centre of the tractor or centrally at the rear so that it can be used for self-propelled work, such as mowing with a Claas Corto three-mower setup. The cab itself can be fitted with either a pneumatic or mechanical suspension system and its position can be changed at the press of a button without the driver having to leave his seat. Four wheel steering, equal size wheels and a fully ballasted weight of 18t make this tractor a real beast! Hydraulic systems are controlled by the CEBIS II computer monitoring system with the rear lift capacity being 11500kg and the front linkage of 7000kg. A brand new Vista cab was introduced on the Xerion by the end of 2005 to bring it in line with the firms combine range.

Claas Ares

The first new tractors to be launched since Renault's takeover by Claas, the 2005 Ares 600 series range featured three models from 116 to 151 maximum horsepower and these were also joined by two 500 Series machines, the biggest of which was the 577ATZ of 123hp. Apart from the new styling updates, included a new gearbox called the Hexashift transmission giving 24 x 24 gears allowing six powershift gears in four ranges. Full cab and front axle suspension is offered as well as the by now standard electronic monitoring and control systems, in this case the TCE 25, 15 or 15T the choice being up to the purchaser.

JCB Fastrac

The 3220 was the biggest Fastrac for only a short while, because in December 2005 JCB launched the mighty Fastrac 8250. With 248hp on tap from its 8.3 litre Cummins QSC six cylinder turbocharged and inter-cooled Tier III compliant diesel engine, this tractor breaks new ground for the Staffordshire firm. Although developed from the 3000 Series chassis and cab, the new 8250 not only features more power but also a CVT transmission, bought from AGCO and called the V-Tronic by JCB, as well as unequal sized wheels and a rear linkage that is capable of lifting 10,000kg. This machine is designed with large arable farmers and contractors in mind and still features a top road speed of up to 65kph.

Case IH Magnum

The arrival of Tier III compliant engines has led to a revamp of the top of the range tractors from CNH. The need for extra cooling has resulted in a bonnet design with more air vents than previously, and the new Magnum range comprises four models from 257 to 345 maximum horsepower from six cylinder, 8.3 litre motors, except the 310 flagship, which has a 9 litre lump. The 280 shown, produces a maximum of 313hp and is fitted with a 19 x 4 full powershift transmission giving a top speed of 50 kph as standard.

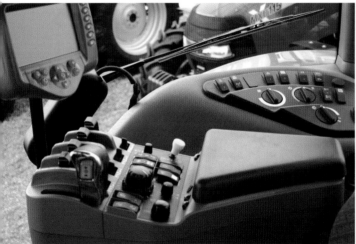

New Holland T8000

Sharing a common platform with the Magnum series, meant that the TG Series from New Holland also faced a revamp. Now designated the T8000 Series the styling remained basically the same, but new 8.3 litre engines were once again to the fore. Three models, the T8040 being the largest, make up the range from 281 to 337 maximum horsepower, driving through either a 19 x 4 Ultra Command full powershift transmission or a 23 x 6 creeper version. Terraglide front axle suspension or tighter turning SuperSteer axle options are available, and up in the cab the new IntelliView monitor screen displays automated functions and tractor settings.

Case IH Steiger STX Quadtrac

This tractor was the very first of the new ultra-powerful Quadtracs into the UK. Now with a rated power output of 530hp increasing to a heady 599 horses under maximum load, this beast is aimed at the latest 600hp leviathans also produced by the likes of John Deere and Challenger. With ever increasing power, how long will it be before 1000hp machines become the norm in the UK? Time will tell!

McCormick MTX150 Diamond Edition

Right: To mark the 60th year of farm machinery manufacture at the firm's Doncaster plant in 2006, 60 examples each of the 102hp CX105 and 152hp MTX150 were finished in this striking silver livery. These tractors were fitted out to full specification including an MP3 player, chrome exhaust, driver's kit, extra work lights and a special certificate. Despite this, McCormick's parent ARGO, announced the closure of the Doncaster plant by the end of 2007, moving production to Italy.

Fendt Vario 300 and 900 Series

Right and below: Fendt updated most of its tractor range for 2007, the four model 300 Vario range consists of tractors from 95 to 125hp, all powered by Deutz four cylinder motors. At the other end of the scale the new flagship 900 Series models have had a complete revamp. The biggest is now the 360hp 936 and features a brand new cab and 7.14 litre Deutz diesel engines, replacing the earlier MAN units. 30, 40 or 60kph top speeds are available depending on buyer's choice. Another new feature is the redesigned front axle suspension system that incorporates an electronic stability control that lets the tractor actually lean into corners. The new cab features a larger glass area, with a single piece door and no pillars to the right.

Landini Powermaster

Based on the same platform as the McCormick XTX Series, the Landini Powermaster range spans three models from 199 to 228hp with power coming from six cylinder 6.75 litre Iveco engines. A semi-powershift transmission is fitted giving eight powershift speeds in four ranges with a creeper option giving a maximum of 48 x 40 speeds. Front axle suspension is fitted as standard but cab suspension is optional. The rear hydraulics have an impressive lift capacity of 10900kg.

John Deere 6030, 7030 & 8030 Series

Replacing the 6020 Series, the 6030 range covers nine models, comprising three four cylinder, 4.5 litre machines, the smallest being 100hp and the largest 120hp with up to 10 extra hp available under load. Half a dozen six cylinder 6.8 litre models make up the rest of the range, with the biggest having an output of 180hp with up to an extra 25hp power boost. All models can be fitted with a mechanical powershift or CVT transmission. The 6030 tractors and the new smaller 7030 tractors (165hp 7430 and 180hp 7530) are built at Mannheim in Germany and utilise the 6030 series chassis frame. However, the heavier duty rear axle and the larger 6.8 litre PowrTech Plus engines are taken from the bigger 7030 machines built in Waterloo, USA. The three Waterloo built 7030 tractors span the power range from 190hp to 220hp, all with an extra power boost of up to 30hp. A choice of a 40kph or 50kph top speed is available along with either semi-powershift or AutoPowr stepless transmissions.

The 8030 Series are larger still with five wheeled and three tracked derivatives on offer. The entry level model is the 8130 at 245hp, while the largest is the 8530 at 360hp and all feature 9.0.litre PowerTech six cylinder John Deere motors. The flagship model has a lift capacity of a whopping 11.762kg, and like the rest of the range can be fitted with the AutoPowr transmission that gives speeds from 50 metres per hour to 42kph. Alternatively, there is the AutoPowershift transmission that offers 16 forward and 5 reverse gears. The Independent Link front suspension system is optional on the 8130, 8230 and 8330, but standard on the 8430 and 8530.

Massey Ferguson 6400 & 7400

The top end of both the 6400 and 7400 Series Massey Ferguson tractors received a facelift, with the top three models in both ranges getting brand new bonnet designs to cover new Sisu 6.6 litre power plants and help airflow. Otherwise they remained pretty much unchanged from the outgoing models, but do point towards the future style of the Massey Ferguson range.

Lamborghini R6

Top left: The whole Lamborghini range now consists of models with the R prefix. The R6 series consists of two Duetz powered four cylinder models of 101 and 120hp and one six cylinder tractor, the R6.110, powered by a 110hp Deutz motor.

Same Iron

Top Right: Equivalent to the Lamborghini R6 range are the new Same Iron Series, consisting of three models from 100 to 120hp with four and six cylinder Deutz engines, just as in the R6 machines. A single lever operates the transmissions four synchro ranges, with buttons to change the three speed powershift along with the two speed splitter.

Deutz Fahr Agrotron180.7

Left: Further up the power range sees the Deutz Fahr Agrotron 180.7, replace the older 165.7 with 170hp from a six cylinder Deutz motor. A ZF 24 x 24 transmission is fitted that can be uprated to 40 x 40 with a creeper box, achieved by six ranges each having four powershift gears in each. The whole tractor weighs in at 11000kg.

Claas Axion

The Axion is the first all-new tractor range from Claas since its takeover of the Renault stable. Five models make up this high horsepower range from the 174hp Axion 810 to the 260hp 850 model. Power comes from six cylinder Deere engines and drives through the Hexashift transmission. Comfort comes with a four point suspension cab as well as a suspended front axle and everything can be monitored and controlled with the CEBIS computerised control centre adopted from the Claas combine range.

Case IH Maxxum

Above and left: MXU styling is used with Case IH's new mid-power tractors that replace some of the MXU and MXM models. Dubbed simply as Maxxum these machines feature the same cab, short wheelbase and sloping bonnet of the MXU tractors, but with power outputs from 100 to 140hp. They also demonstrate the new corporate image for Case IH featuring a red 'i' in the IH logo, which is part of a new direction for the CNH group, where brand identities between the Case IH and New Holland ranges are to be separated and not based as closely on the same common platform. Production of these new Maxxum tractors has also been moved from Basildon in Essex to St. Valentin in Austria, the home of Steyr tractor production and the new base for the Case IH brand.

New Holland T6000

Left and below: Back in the blue corner and the brand new T6000 Series replaces the older TSA range. Still featuring the Horizon cab, the T6000 Series is made up of six models with three four cylinder models from the 101hp T6010 to the 134hp T6040, and three six cylinder models from the 117hp T6030 to the 141hp T6070. The T6040 stands out from the rest as the only model with engine power management that boosts maximum power up to a heady 151hp from its four cylinder motor, making this the only tractor in the Elite version of the T6000 range. The other models are available in either the basic Delta version or the Plus higher spec alternative. Terraglide front axle suspension is optional on all models while the Comfort Ride cab suspension is only standard on the T6040, optional on the others.

New Holland T7000

Four models make up the New Holland T7000 Series featuring new six cylinder 6.75 litre engines. Built in the Basildon factory the range spans from 165hp T7030 to the 210hp T7060, with a power boost on each to provide more horsepower when required. Featuring the Horizon cab first seen on the TSA range, New Holland claim that when fitted to the T7000 Series, it is the quietest cab on the market at only 69 dBA at the driver's ear, a feat also made possible by the design of the T7000 Series new engines. IntelliView II is the computer monitor and control system fitted to the new tractors that checks all the diagnostics such as engine power output and fuel usage. SuperSteer, with its 65 degree turning circle can be fitted, as well as Terralock headland management system, that disengages the diff locks and the four wheel drive when the front wheels are turned past a certain angle, and will re-engage when the wheels return to a straight position. Also, the T7000 can be specified with the Fast Steer steering aid, which allows quicker lock to lock turning by simply pressing an inner steering wheel, mounted inside the main steering wheel itself, and only moving it a few degrees will actually turn the front wheels onto full lock. This was a feature first found on the TSA range but only now at this higher horsepower bracket with the launch of the New Holland T7000 Series tractors.

Index

The Tractor Story v. 1 True Classics

Tractors of the 1960's, 70's and 80's. This first volume of The Tractor Story features machines from that magical era the nineteen sixties, seventies and eighties – the True Classics.

Special features within the programme look at the rise in popularity of four-wheel drive machines such as County, Muir Hill and Roadless and we meet David Brown owners, highlighting the 990, 885 and 1394. *Duration: 75 mins.*

The Tractor Story v. 2 Modern Marvels

Tractors of the 1990's and the 21st Century with Jonathan Whitlam and Stephen Richmond.
We bring The Tractor Story right up to date by featuring machines from the 1990's up to the first five years of the 21st Century. The DVD features tactors that simply bristle with electronics, suspension systems, revolutionary transmissions and luxury working environments – tractors that certainly deserve the title – MODERN MARVELS. *Duration: 114 mins*

The Tractor Story v. 3 Vintage Power

Horses, Steam and the First Fifty years of Tractors with Jonathan Whitlam and Stephen Richmond
In the third volume of The Tractor Story horses, steam traction engines and ploughing engines share the stage with the first early tractors. We see how the tractors developed from basic pulling machines to the more sophisticated tractors of the 1950's and 60's. Many classic tractor names from this era are seen both working and at Cheffins Vintage auctions. *Duration: 100 mins.*

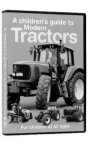

A Children's Guide to Modern Tractors

They can be big and they can be small but have you ever wondered what tractors are really like and what they can actually do? This programme will show you just how amazing modern tractors really are!

With quizzes, close-ups and a fascinating narration this programme is a colourful, action packed and instructive sixty minutes of tractor action that will keep tractor fans of all ages happily glued to the screen. *Duration: 60 mins.*

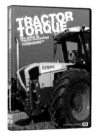

Tractor Torque

The Very Latest In Tractor Technology. Stephen and Jonathan analyse the very latest tractor models. This also gives you, the viewer a chance to choose which machines you think are the most revolutionary of all.

Watch countless different tractor models hard at work, highlights include the Claas Xerion 3300, Valtra's reverse drive S280, McCormick's brand new XTX range, New Holland's TVT series and the JCB Fastrac 3220 to name but a few. *Duration: 100 mins.*

The Tractor's Companion Machinery on the Farm

Vol. One – Sow and Scatter
Vol. Two – Harvest and Gather
The tractor on its own is a wonderfully versatile machine but when an implement of any kind is attached, its usefulness doubles. These comprehensive programmes cover most processes from preparing the soil through to the final task of harvesting the crops. *Duration vol 1 - 80mins, vol 2 - 105mins.*

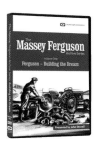

The Massey Ferguson Archive Series v. 1

'Ferguson – Building the Dream'
Volume one begins with a look at the revolutionary Ferguson Type A and the highly successful Ford-Ferguson tractors that first appeared in 1939 with rare original footage of them at work in glorious colour. We see the TE20 working with various implements as well as the complete manufacturing process at the famous factory in Banner Lane, Coventry. *Duration: 100 mins*

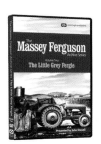

The Massey Ferguson Archive Series v. 2

'The Little Grey Fergie'
Volume two concentrates on the Ferguson TE20 tractor, often lovingly referred to as "The Little Grey Fergie". Films from the late forties and early fifties transport us back to a time when farming life was very different from today. The TE20 is shown at work all over the British Isles using a range of Ferguson implements. *Duration: 82 mins*

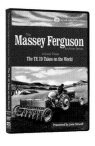

The Massey Ferguson Archive Series v. 3

'The TE 20 Takes on the World'
Volume Three looks once again at the famous Ferguson TE20 with four films showing just how versatile the Little Grey Fergie really was, with films shot in countries around the world and in Britain. We also look at how the TE20 came to the rescue after the terrible 1953 floods on the east coast of England and Scotland. *Duration: 92 mins*

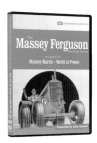

The Massey Ferguson Archive Series v. 4

'Massey Harris – World of Power'
The films in this programme show Massey Harris tractors, implements and combine harvesters at work all over the globe, as well as a close look at the company's tractor range. They were shot in colour and date from the 1940's giving an exceptional glimpse of farming practices sixty years ago! *Duration: 82 mins*

The Ferguson Revolution

The story of Harry Ferguson, his tractors, implements and hydraulic system.
This is without doubt a genuinely comprehensive account and lasting tribute to a man with amazing foresight and brilliance who devised a system that is now an integral part of tractor design in the 21st century. *Duration: 104 mins.*

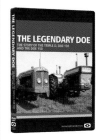

The Legendary Doe

The Story of the Doe Triple D, the Doe 130 and the Doe 150.
The Legendary Doe tells the story of the Doe Triple D, the 130 & 150, the famous tandem tractors produced by Essex agricultural dealers, Ernest Doe & Sons. It includes both modern and archive Doe footage, with Alan Doe's entire unique archive film shot in 1960. The Doe Triple D caused a huge stir back in the late fifties and we see how this amazing machine still turns heads today. *Duration: 100 minutes*

Ford and Fordson Showcase - Cork Ireland April 2006

Nearly 200 Ford and Fordson tractors covering all eras, converged on Cork, Ireland, to make what was the largest single manufacture tractor event ever held in the country. If you were not lucky enough to be there, this programme is your chance to witness one of the most spectacular gatherings of Ford and Fordson tractors ever seen – a totally unforgettable experience!
Duration: 72 mins

Ireland's Tribute To Ford

The Ford and Fordson Showcase
This is the incredible story of the 2007 Ford and Fordson Showcase, held in the historic city of Cork, Ireland. We capture all the weekends action including the amazing Saturday evening tractor run around this wonderful city. A huge variety of Ford and Fordson tractors took part and with this massive number all assembled at one venue it really is Ireland's Tribute to Ford tractors. *Duration: 60 mins.*

Monsters Of the Beet Field - The Story of the Sugar Beet Harvester.

Using contemporary, archive and manufacturers' footage, Stephen and Jonathan guide us on a journey through the development of the sugar beet harvester - from horse and man power to automatic, electronically controlled mega machines.
Four special features are included. This story travels from the smallest beginnings right up to the Monsters of the Beet Field. *Duration: 98 mins.*

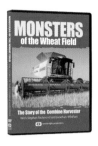

Monsters of the Wheat Field - The Story of the Combine Harvester

Like the Beet story; contemporary, archive and manufacturers' footage is used as we travel on a fascinating journey through the story of the combine harvester, after the tractor the most iconic item of farm machinery. From the earliest reaper-binders to the largest combine in the world – the Claas Lexion 600 – this programme brings together more working combine harvesters in one film than ever before!
Duration: 94 minutes

Hi-Tech Tractors

with Jonathan Whitlam and Stephen Richmond.
Jonathan and Stephen scrutinize the newest models from the major manufacturers, talking to the dealers about the latest sophisticated technology on these amazing new tractors. The programme also includes a special feature on various designs of suspension and a section looking at tractors with crawler tracks. All this plus over thirty different machines hard at work in their natural environment:
Duration 60 mins.

 ## second sight productions

Second Sight Productions aim to produce quality 'Countryside' books and DVD programmes that the viewer will find interesting, informative and accurate as well as entertaining. To view our extensive range of titles please go to:-

www.secondsightproductions.co.uk

to find out the latest news and information including full programme and book descriptions, accompanying photographs and online purchasing facilities.
Or telephone 01621 817114 for a free brochure. Orders can be sent with a cheque to:- Station House, 1 Station Road, Tiptree, Essex CO5 0AD